Handbook for Observing the SATELLITES

N. E. Howard

Handbook for Observing the SATELLITES

Thomas Y. Crowell Company

New York · Established 1834

ACKNOWLEDGMENTS

I should like to express my very deep appreciation to the following people for their great help in making this little book possible:

To the members of the Millbrook School Moonwatch Team who showed by example that one doesn't need to be a professional astronomer to chase satellites successfully.

To Mr. Rene Clark and the Millbrook School Photo Service, who are responsible for most of the photographs.

To Mr. Woldemar Neufeld for his production of some of the drawings used.

To Hunt Stockwell for the jacket photograph.

N.E.H.

Preface

When the history of the twentieth century is written, one of the red-letter dates will be October 4, 1957. On that day the first man-made satellite appeared in the skies. The eyes of the world were turned toward the heavens, and people crowded around short-wave radios, listening for the "beeps" which gave notice that man was at last standing on the threshold of space. Possibly no other scientific achievement thus far in our century so captured the imagination of the public or evoked such a response.

Everywhere people banded together to look for some particular aspect of this satellite and those which followed. Operation Moonwatch, an organization already set up by the Smithsonian Astrophysical Observatory to locate satellites visually, was besieged by applications from new teams. Operation Moonbeam came into being to track the satellites by means of their radio signals, and Operation Phototrack was organized to track them photographically. Each group operates under specific conditions and procedures; each has a membership of individuals who hope that in some way their efforts will be of some use in the most extensive scientific effort of our century.

But there are also the thousands who follow the satellites just because they are exciting. There are the watchers who crowd the outskirts of Cape Canaveral in the hope that, against the roar of the giant rockets, they may see a satellite-bearing missile slowly nose its way into the sky on a trip that may last a hundred years. And there also are those of us who watch the skies from our front lawns or back doorsteps hoping to get a glimpse of a satellite as it streaks past on one of its nearly endless trips around the earth.

This book is written for the latter group. It is based on the assumption that knowing the how and why of satellites makes looking for them more fun. The questions it attempts to answer are those actually asked by would-be satellite-watchers in training and observing sessions of a Moonwatch team. The suggested techniques and methods have been tried out successfully on the satellites themselves. The equipment described in it was made and used for the specific purpose of watching satellites.

We shall have the satellites with us for a long time. A short time ago the earth had only one moon; today it has more than the planet Uranus; tomorrow, who knows?

Contents

Chapter 1

On Satellites in General

Most of us think of the satellites as the most important scientific contribution of our century, and quite justifiably we have great admiration for those whose ingenuity and imagination have made them possible. Yet long before the Wright brothers made their historic launching at Kitty Hawk, long before Robert Fulton invented the steamboat, even before James Watt discovered the principle of the steam engine, a man named Isaac Newton had considered the possibilities of satellites and named the conditions that make them possible. Nearly three hundred years ago, in the greatest book on science ever to come from the pen of man, *Principia Mathematica,* he discussed the conditions under which a projectile must be launched to follow a given orbit and laid down the precise mathematics of orbital motion. He foresaw rocket propulsion and clearly stated the theory behind it. He took into account the effect of air resistance on a satellite and predicted that, if it passed over bulges on the earth, it would wander from its path because of the varying gravitational forces acting on it. In short, he did everything except manufacture and fire a satellite-containing rocket. And he was not far from doing that, too, because in his remarkable book one may find a drawing showing how a satellite could be fired from a cannon placed on a mountain top.

NEWTON'S LAWS

The satellites which circle our globe today obey the laws that Newton discovered. If we wish to understand more about their behavior and the forces that act upon them, we have only to turn back to Newton's writings to find a full explanation. When a satellite leaves the earth under the lash of the furious combination of nitric acid with hydrazine, or some other equally potent fuel, it gains speed until it attains the unbelievable rate of 18,000 miles per hour, or almost five miles per second. If, when it reaches this speed at a height of three hundred miles or so, it has been guided into a path parallel to the earth's surface, it will continue in an orbit around the earth. But what keeps a satellite moving after its fuel burns out? Why the speed of 18,000 miles an hour? Why doesn't it fall immediately? Why do we choose a height of three hundred miles to place it in orbit? What determines how long a satellite will remain in its orbit before it comes streaking back to earth?

Let's answer these questions one at a time. Perhaps the one most commonly asked is, what keeps a satellite moving? We are inclined to think that the natural state for an object is one of rest since, in our experience, all moving bodies come to rest after a longer or shorter time. Consequently we find it hard to believe that an object, once put in motion, won't slow down by itself after a while. But Newton's First Law of Motion says that a body at rest tends to continue at rest, while one in motion (in the absence of friction) continues to move in a straight line. In other words, if one were to roll a perfectly smooth and frictionless bowling ball down an equally frictionless alley of infinite length, the ball would roll on forever.

Most of us have had the experience, at one time or another, of trying to push an automobile. The auto seems to resist being pushed while it is

Sir Isaac Newton.

standing still; but, once it starts moving, the force we must apply to keep it going is much less than that required to get it started. If we now wish to stop the automobile, we find we must again use a large amount of force.

To explain this, Newton declared that it is the fundamental nature of mass to resist change in the state it happens to be in at the moment. If it is motionless, it tends to remain that way. If moving, it resists slowing down or speeding up. Newton called this characteristic of matter its inertia. Satellites have inertia and, once started on their way, will go on forever unless they bump into something or are acted upon by a force that slows them down. Once we place a satellite outside the atmosphere where there is practically no air to impede it, the only remaining objects that could interfere with it are meteorites. Even though meteorites are, for the most part, smaller than a grain of sand, a satellite striking very many of them will lose speed.

Newton's First Law also states that moving objects continue to move in a straight line. If this is true, why doesn't a satellite go roaring off into space once it has been turned parallel to the earth's surface? To answer this question, we turn to another of Newton's laws, the Law of Universal Gravitation. Stated mathematically: two objects attract each other with a force directly proportional to their masses, and inversely proportional to the square of the distance between them. Put more simply, two objects always exert a pull on each other, and the strength of this pull depends upon how heavy they are. Moreover, the pull becomes less if the distance between the two objects increases. If the distance becomes twice as great, the pull is one-quarter as much. If, on the other hand, the distance decreases to one-third its former value, the pull is now nine times as great.

Now, the mass of the earth is inconceivably great compared to that of a satellite, so the result of the earth's gravitational force is to pull the satellite toward it. Consequently, when the satellite settles into its 18,000-mile-an-hour speed, the straight line it would ordinarily follow is bent toward the earth. If this bending is exactly the right amount in proportion to the speed of the satellite, the result will be an orbit and the satellite will circle the globe. If the bending of the path is too much, it will come streaking back toward the earth's surface. When the bending is not enough, it will move farther away and will head out toward the limitless reaches of space.

These three factors—weight, speed, and distance from the earth—determine the fate of the satellite. The first factor—how much a satellite weighs —is not very important. Compared to the immense weight of the earth (if we expressed it in tons, we should have to write the figure 6 followed by twenty-one zeros), all satellites weigh about the same and are pulled toward the earth the same amount. Consequently, a house and a feather could circle the earth in the same orbit and at the same speed if there were no air resistance at all. But, as Newton's Law indicates, the distance from the earth and the speed depend heavily upon each other; and the closer the satellite is to the earth, the faster it must go to avoid being dragged down to the earth's surface. If, for example, we wish it to remain at an average distance of 350 miles from the earth, we must give it a speed of 4.5 miles per second. At 1,100 miles we need give it a speed of 4.4 miles per second, and at 4,000 miles its speed must be 3.7 miles per second. Our largest satellite, the moon, pokes along at only two-thirds of a mile per second at its remote average distance of 240,000 miles.

Perhaps the most interesting distance at which we could place a baby moon would be 22,300 miles, for here it would revolve around the earth once every 24 hours. Since the earth is turning at this speed itself, the satellite would appear to be motionless in the sky. If its orbit was directly over the equator and the spot chosen for the satellite to "hover" was due south of San Antonio, Texas, it could be seen all over the United States. For observers in Maine or the state of Washington it would appear low on the horizon, while from the southern tier of states it would be high in the sky. Conversely, an observer placed on the satellite could shift his attention from events happening in Carson City, Nevada, to the goings-on in Carson City, Michigan, simply by shifting his telescope a few degrees.

Most of us find it easy to visualize the idea of a speeding body held in an orbit by a definite restraining force and can understand without much difficulty the mechanics of a ball whirled around one's head at the end of a string. The ball is prevented from flying off into space by the string. But the idea of invisible forces holding two objects in position is more difficult to swallow. However, we can perform a simple experiment that will demonstrate the reality of these invisible forces. We need a piece of glass about a foot square, a strong bar magnet, and a small ball bearing. We place the glass on supports so that it is perfectly level and there is enough room under it to stand the magnet on end with its upper end just touching the glass. It makes no difference which pole of the magnet is uppermost.

Now we place the ball bearing near the edge of the glass and give it a

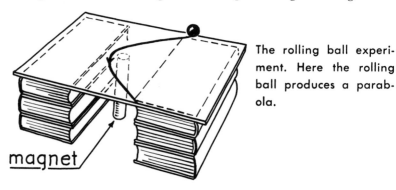

The rolling ball experiment. Here the rolling ball produces a parabola.

slight push toward the center, aiming it just to one side of the magnet. After some experimenting with direction and speed, we can make the ball bearing behave in several ways. If we use too much speed, it will roll right past the magnet. With a little less speed, it will be drawn toward the magnet, and will roll past it on a curved course. A still gentler push makes it curve all the way around and return toward the starting place. If we succeed in doing this we will have duplicated the curve many comets take as they go around the sun. Finally, with just the right amount of push, the ball will orbit around the end of the magnet in an elliptical path. We notice that the ball speeds up as it goes close to the magnet and that the farther away it is the slower it rolls.

This little experiment has several implications. For one thing, it demonstrates the idea of "escape velocity." We have already seen that the greater the orbit, the slower a satellite travels. If the ball is given too much of a push, it goes on past the magnet with very little deviation in its path. Similarly, if a satellite is started from its launching pad and gains too much speed, the attraction of the earth's gravitational field will be insufficient to turn it into an orbit and it will fly off into space. The speed at which an object escapes completely from the earth's gravitation is called its escape velocity and is 25,000 miles per hour, or a little over 7 miles per second.

Since the gravitational force varies with the mass of a planet or other heavenly body, we should not expect escape velocity to be the same all over the solar system. If we were to make a trip to Mars, we would need rockets capable of boosting our speed to 7 miles per second to get away from the earth, but on the return trip we could cut down the power enough to hold our speed to only 3.2 miles per second and still get away from Mars's gravitational field. On the moon we require a speed of only 1.5 miles per second. But for an object to escape from the sun it would have to attain a velocity of 383 miles per second.

Let us do the rolling ball experiment again, this time having sprinkled a little lycopodium powder or talcum powder on the glass so we can examine the path the ball takes. If the ball rolls a little too fast and doesn't orbit around the end of the magnet, it will make a curved path which, when we compare it to the curves found in a textbook on analytic geometry, will be a parabola. If we try again, this time giving it just the right amount of speed and direction to put it in orbit, it will travel in what appears to be a circular path. But when we examine the path more closely, we will see that it is a flattened circle, or ellipse, and that the magnet appears inside one end of this figure, not at the center. Again we notice that the ball rolls most slowly when it is farthest from the point of attraction and most swiftly when it is closest to it. In fact, the ball is rolling in a path that is in accordance with another law of motion discovered even before Newton's time.

JOHANNES KEPLER AND THE SATELLITES

The great astronomer Johannes Kepler, who spent most of his life observing the planets and their motions, made several very important discoveries concerning their orbits. These discoveries apply to the satellites of today because any smaller body revolving around a larger one is a satellite, whether it is the moon or an artificial satellite revolving around the earth, or the planets around the sun.

Kepler noticed first that the orbit of a satellite is always an ellipse. Before we talk very much about elliptical orbits we should take a little time to talk about ellipses themselves.

An ellipse is difficult to draw freehand but can be produced easily by using two pins and a short piece of thread. We push the pins, about three inches apart, into a piece of cardboard. Then we make a loop by tying the ends of a seven-inch piece of thread together and place it over the pins. If the point of a pencil is placed inside the loop and moved until the thread is taut against the pins, and the pencil is moved around the pins, always keeping the thread taut, an ellipse will be traced on the cardboard by the point of the pencil. The two points where the pins pierce the cardboard are called the foci of the ellipse. If the pins are placed farther apart the ellipse is flattened; but if they are moved nearer each other the figure becomes more nearly round. If they are so close that they can be replaced by a single pin, the figure becomes a circle. It can be seen from this that the circle is therefore only a special kind of ellipse, and it follows that the orbit of a satellite could, theoretically, be a circle. In practice this does not happen, for reasons we discuss later; and all the satellites thus far launched move in elliptical paths with the center of the earth at one of the foci.

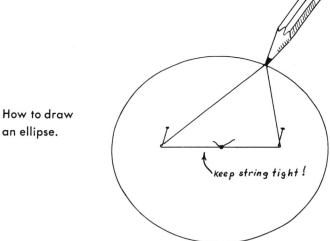

How to draw
an ellipse.

keep string tight !

6

Kepler also made another discovery that is very useful in determining he speed of a satellite at any point in its orbit. Stated as simply as possible, it is that a line drawn from either focus of an ellipse to a body revolving around this focus will sweep over equal areas of space in equal intervals of time. Such a line will be shortest when the body is at one end of the ellipse and longest at the other. For the areas to be equal, the distance the body travels at the short end must be greater than that at the long end. Hence the speed must be greater at the shorter distance. This is confirmed by what we observed with our rolling ball.

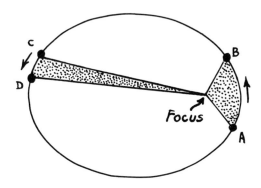

Kepler's Second Law. The area swept over from A to B is equal to the area from C to D in the same time interval. Therefore the satellite goes fastest between A and B.

Another discovery of Kepler's, called his Third Law, is a special application of Newton's Law of Universal Gravitation. It states that the square of the period of a satellite (time for one revolution around the earth) is proportional to the cube of its distance from the center of the earth. Stripped of its mathematics, this means that the closer a satellite is to the surface of our globe, the shorter is the period of a complete revolution. This explains what otherwise might be a puzzling aspect of the behavior of satellites. Because of air resistance, they eventually slow down and are gradually pulled toward the earth. But when this happens, the time of revolution becomes less. Sputnik II, for example, started its existence in an orbit that carried it once around the earth in 104 minutes. Just before it plunged into the Caribbean, however, it was circling the globe in only 87 minutes.

This consequence of the Third Law is often seen in situations that have nothing to do with satellites. We have all seen a figure skater with her arms extended, rotating slowly on the ice. As she pulls her arms in closer to her body she whirls ever faster until finally she spins like a top. When she wishes to slow down she simply opens her arms again. We can do the same

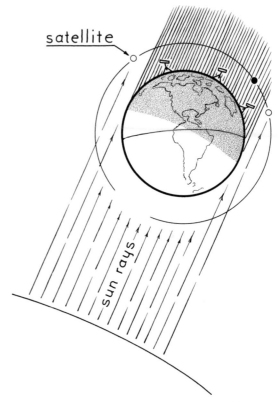

satellite

sun rays

Why we see the satellite at twilight.

thing with a piano stool. One sits on the stool with arms and legs extended as far as possible while a friend starts the stool rotating. The moment the arms are pulled in, the rotational speed increases very considerably. Try it sometime, but be prepared to be tossed off the stool by the speed generated.

There are other puzzling characteristics of satellites as well as their variations in speed. One of the questions most commonly asked is why we can see them only in the twilight periods before dawn and after sunset. Those who have seen a high mountain peak shining in sunlight after the surrounding land becomes shadowed by deepening dusk will understand why a satellite is still brilliantly illuminated long after the sun has set. The earth beneath the satellite has passed into the shadow cast by the lifting horizon for, as we all know, the turning earth makes it seem as though the horizon were lifting. The satellite, riding high in the heavens, is still fully exposed to the rays of the sun. Eventually the spinning earth throws its obscuring shadow high enough so that the satellite becomes lost in it. And since the tiny object has no light of its own it becomes invisible to earth-bound watchers. One day, no doubt, we shall develop batteries powerful enough to give sufficient electricity to illuminate the satellite itself as well as to run its equipment. Then we can watch it whirl above us all through the night. But until that time we must limit our observations to the twilight hours after dusk and before dawn.

During daylight hours we can't see the satellite because the multitudes of tiny dust particles in the atmosphere reflect enough sunlight to blind us to the satellite's faint gleam. This also explains why the stars and planets are hidden during the day.

To many of us it seems impossible that we can see a tiny object only a few feet in diameter at a distance of hundreds of miles. And our doubts are justified; we can't. But we can see the light reflected from its highly polished surface. In the days before telephone and radio, fire watchers on mountaintops many miles distant from one another could send messages back and forth by means of a little gadget called a heliograph. This was simply a small mirror, and the rays of the sun were reflected from one observer to the other. The mirrors themselves were invisible—so, even, were the fire towers from which the messages were sent—but the brilliant flashes of sunlight traveled the tremendous distances with ease. For this reason the surfaces of satellites are made of a highly reflective metal, and the "objects" we see in the sky are nothing more than the rays of the sun which bounce back to us.

Another puzzling characteristic of the satellites is that they appear to change direction. We see one, for example, traveling across the sky from north to south, and a few hours later (if we're lucky) see it again, but this time it is going in the opposite direction. A satellite in a north-south orbit does, of course, travel southward during half its orbit, but after it reaches the southernmost point of its orbit it heads north for the remaining half. Which way it appears to be going when we see it depends upon which half of its orbit we happen to be under at the time.

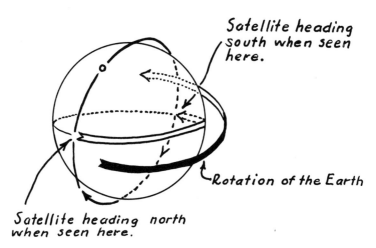

Satellite heading south when seen here.

Rotation of the Earth

Satellite heading north when seen here.

Some readers may want to skip this section. But those who would like a more detailed discussion of how astronomers plot the orbit and predict the appearance of a satellite should read this section carefully. This is not a complete treatment, of course, since the mathematical determination of satellite orbits is too complicated to discuss here.

As more and more satellites make their appearance in the sky, the terms used to describe their orbits will become more common. We may as well familiarize ourselves with at least some of them; and, if we follow the diagrams carefully as each term is presented, this should not be too difficult.

We have already seen that all satellites travel in elliptical orbits around the earth, and that the center of the earth is at one focus of the ellipse. In the accompanying diagram, the center of the earth and one of the foci of the ellipse are the same point, F. The *major axis* of the orbit is the line AB, half of which is the *semimajor axis AC* (or a). Similarly, the *minor axis* and the *semiminor axis* are the lines DE and DC respectively. The point where the orbit comes closest to the earth is the point B, called the *perigee* (*peri* = near; *ge* = earth), and where it is farthest away is the *apogee* (*apo* = far) point, or point A.

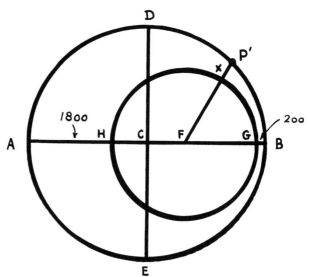

The distance from the center of the earth to the center of the orbit depends upon the *eccentricity* of the orbit. This eccentricity, designated by the letter e, is a number always less than one, and is chosen so that, when it is multiplied by the length of the semimajor axis, it will determine the actual distance of the center of the earth from the center of the elliptical orbit. To use a rough example, suppose AC is 5,000 miles and the eccentricity of the orbit is 0.16. Then F will be distant from the center of the orbit by an amount equal to 0.16×5000, or 800 miles.

Now if the earth's radius is 4,000 miles, we have

$AC = CB = 5000$, or $CB - (CF + FG) = GB$. Substituting, $5000 - (800 + 4000) = 200$, or the perigee distance.

Similarly,

$AC - (HF - CF) = AH$, or $5000 - (4000 - 800) = 1800$, or the apogee distance.

Let us suppose that the satellite is at point P' in its orbit. Its distance above an observer at point X, then, must be somewhere between 200 and 1,800 miles.

A close look at the figure will show that the angle $P'FB$ defines the position of the satellite. This angle is called the *true anomaly* and is a measure of the distance of the satellite from its perigee point. This perigee point, or position, is very important in the determination of the orbit. Its angular distance from the place where the satellite crosses the equatorial plane is represented by the letter ω. The distance of the satellite from the center of the earth is measured along the line FP', and is called the *radius vector*. Other terms applicable here are the *complete time for one revolution, P;* the average angular motion, or *mean motion, n;* and the *time of the perigee passage, T.* The small letter t is used to denote *any instant of time* during one revolution.

In the next diagram we shall find one or two terms used by scientists and newspapermen alike in talking about satellites. The *inclination of the orbit* is one of them. It is designated by the letter i and is a measure of the angle the orbit makes with the equator of the earth, or the angle between

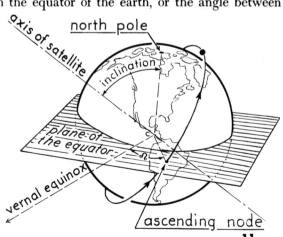

The satellite's nodes and inclination.

the polar axis of the earth and the axis of the orbit. Another expression, the *nodal passage,* is a little more difficult to understand. In order to do so, we must imagine a plane passing through the earth's equator and extending into space. A satellite must pass through this plane twice in one complete revolution. The passage from south to north cuts the plane at a point called the *ascending node.* The angle between this point, as seen from the earth, and a fixed location in the heavens called the *vernal equinox* determines the position of the satellite in space when it passes through the ascending node. This position is called the *right ascension* of the ascending node and has the symbol Ω.

Measurement of these six variables—the semimajor axis (a), the eccentricity (e), the right ascension of the ascending node (Ω), the time of perigee passage (T), the inclination (i), and the position of the perigee point (ω)—fix the position of the satellite in space for any given instant of time.

The position of the observer, at his fixed point on the spinning earth, can also be determined for the same instant of time. These two positions—

HARVARD COLLEGE OBSERVATORY
ANNOUNCEMENT CARD 1390

Satellite 1958a. — The U.S.A. National Committee for the International Geophysical Year has announced that an instrumented earth satellite was placed in orbit on February 1, 3^h 55^m 05^s U.T. at a point approximately 25.84 N and 73.61 W. It was launched by a U.S. Army Jupiter C rocket on February 1, 3^h 48^m U.T. from Cape Canaveral, Florida at 28.5 N and 80.6 W.

Including the empty rocket casing of the last stage, the satellite weighs about 30 lbs, is cylindrical in shape with a length of 80 inches and a diameter of 6 inches. It contains two radio transmitters; amplitude modulated transmission at 108.03 mc with power level of 50 milliwatts; phase modulated transmission at 108.0 mc with power level of 10 milliwatts; telemetry of data by both transmitters.

The surface of the satellite is white and may be visible with binoculars under optimum conditions. Scientific experiments include cosmic ray observations, meteoric impact, and temperature measurements.

Comet 1957f. — Dr. Henry L. Giclas has sent the following position of Comet 1957f:

	a	δ	d
	(1957.0)	(1957.0)	
U.T.	$21^h13^m57^s94$	$-37°45'49''.3$	25.15350
1957 October			

Mag. 10   Diffuse without central condensation.

FRED L. WHIPPLE

February 1, 1958

HARVARD COLLEGE OBSERVATORY
ANNOUNCEMENT CARD 1393

Satellite 1958a. — Dr. Paul Herget and Dr. Raynor L. Duncombe of the Naval Research Laboratory, Washington, D.C. have obtained the following preliminary orbital elements for Satellite 1958a from analysis of Minitrack observations extending over the first 32 revolutions, for 3^h 58^m U.T. on February 1, 1958:

Minimum Height	219 miles
Maximum Height	1587 miles
Period	114.95 minutes
Eccentricity	0.14052
Inclination	33.58
Longitude of Ascending Node	342.95 (motion −4.26 per day)
Argument of Perigee	120.76 (motion +6.31 per day)
Mean Anomaly at Epoch	14.68
Semi-major Axis	1.2278 earth radii

The following optical observations of Satellite 1958a have been received from Moonwatch teams:

Date February	Time U.T.	Position R.A.	Dec.	Type of Obs.
2	24^h 45^m 54^s	Alamogordo, New Mexico (Lat. 32° 52′ 24″ N Long. 105° 57′ 02″ W) $52°$ $24°$ N $44°$ 54^m ±5^m	+33° 06′	vis. +8 mag.
3	14^h 44^m 16^s	Manhattan, Kansas (Lat. 39° 09′.75 N Long. 96° 28′.85 W) 5^h 37^m	−1° 40′	vis. +5 mag.
3	3^h 46^m 10^s	Alamogordo, New Mexico (Lat. 32° 52′ 24″ N Long. 105° 57′ 02″ W) 5^h 23^m	+14° 54′	vis. +8 mag.
6	24^h 24^m 42^s	China Lake, California (Lat. 35.657 N Long. 117.663 W) Az. N 177.25 E	Alt. 71°	vis.

February 6, 1958

FRED L. WHIPPLE

How satellites are announced. (Used by permission)

of the satellite and the observer—are worked out using the same system of coordinates for each. Based on the results of the calculation, the information supplied to the observer will let him know if it is possible to see the satellite in any particular passage, and if so, where to look for it. It is small wonder that centers such as the Smithsonian Astrophysical Observatory, which compute the orbits of the satellites and predict their passages, must resort to supercomputers such as the IBM 704 to accomplish this task.

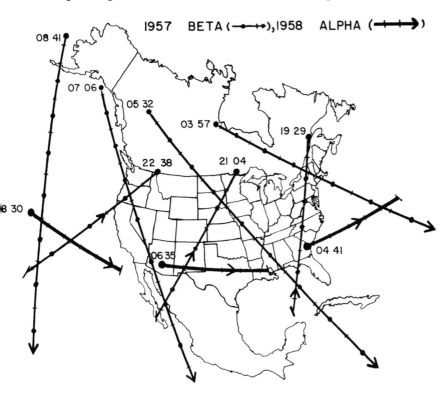

This shows the passages of two satellites, 1957 beta (Sputnik II) and 1958 alpha (Explorer I), March 19, 1958. All times E.S.T. (Courtesy Smithsonian Astrophysical Observatory)

PERTURBATIONS OF A SATELLITE

Calculations based on the factors we have just talked about determine an *ideal* orbit for a satellite. But this is not the real orbit it will follow, since there are several other factors that must be taken into consideration. These are called *perturbations*, or influences that cause the satellite to wander from the ideal path set up by the mathematicians.

If the earth were a perfect sphere with its mass centered at one point, it would not be difficult to determine the ideal path taken by a satellite in its mad dash. Unfortunately, the earth is not a perfect sphere. It has a small bulge around the equator and its poles are slightly flattened. These factors influence the satellite, for the equatorial bulge creates an extra gravitational pull as the equator is approached. The result is a rotation of the whole satellite orbit in a westerly direction (called *precession*) similar to the motion of a hoop when it spins like a top. With the third-stage rocket of the first Russian satellite, the result of this extra pull was to force the orbit to move westward at a rate of 3.25° per day. This is in addition to the apparent westward movement of the orbit resulting from the earth's rotation. Here is another difficulty, for the equatorial bulge of the earth is not known exactly. One of the reasons for launching a satellite is to determine just how much increase in waistline the earth has acquired since its youth.

Precession of the orbit.

The present value, a 1/297 increase over the circumference based on a perfect sphere, is used to calculate the probable deviation of the orbit. The problem is then worked backward, and the actual circumference can theoretically be found from the observed variance from the predicted orbit.

Another effect of the earth's bulge is to cause the perigee point to move along the orbit in the same way that a bulge on the tire of a bicycle makes the tire creep around the rim of the wheel. But the orbit is not a circle;

it is an ellipse. The movement just described will change the period of revolution slightly, and this has to be taken into consideration in orbital predictions.

The factor that has the most marked influence on the orbit is air resistance. Our atmosphere thins rapidly as we ascend from the earth. At 10 miles it is only one-tenth as heavy as it is at sea level, at 60 miles only one-millionth as heavy, and at 200 miles it decreases to a value of one million-millionth of what it is on the earth. Nevertheless, these few remaining molecules of air have an effect on even a thousand-pound satellite. Although one would expect the perigee point to be most affected, since the air is so much thicker nearer the earth, it is the apogee distance which actually decreases the greater amount. The tendency of the orbit, as the apogee descends, is to pass from an ellipse to a circle, where apogee and perigee are almost equal. When this happens, the satellite nears the end of its career and is ready for the fiery plunge through the atmosphere which causes its destruction.

The function of the astronomer-mathematician is to link the satellite's wandering path due to the perturbations in its orbit with the fixed path it would follow if these perturbations did not exist. The two can be blended into one generalized orbit by mathematical means. This orbit will not be the real one, but it will be close enough for practical purposes.

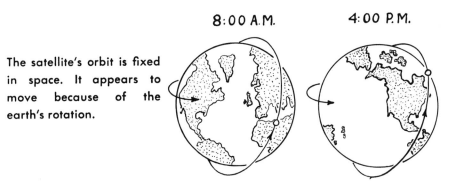

8:00 A.M.   **4:00 P.M.**

The satellite's orbit is fixed in space. It appears to move because of the earth's rotation.

We must realize that, except for perturbations, the orbit of a satellite is fixed in space. It is a flat plane which has a rim defined by the satellite's path and which slices through the center of the earth. From our viewpoint, however, the orbit appears to move, for the earth is turning inside the orbit like a basketball spinning in a hoop. Rotation toward the east turns the earth completely around once every twenty-four hours, or through 15°

in one hour. If a satellite, circling the earth in 90 minutes, appeared over New York during one passage, it would show up over Omaha, Nebraska, on its next trip.

In spite of all these factors it is possible to set up a table of satellite appearances on the basis of only a few early sightings, provided they are accurate enough. These time schedules are of great importance to would-be satellite watchers, for by their use we can predict where and how often we may be able to see the satellites ourselves.

SMITHSONIAN ASTROPHYSICAL OBSERVATORY, CAMBRIDGE, MASSACHUSETTS
January 29, 1958

These predictions are based on the following orbital elements obtained on January 28, 1958:

Time of nodal passage = $386.06347 + 0.068980$ N $- 1.636 \times 10^{-6} \times$ N^2
Right ascension of ascending node = $259°8 - 2°87 (t - 386) - 0°0017 (t - 386)^2$
Argument of perigee = $34° - 0°3 (t - 386)$
Semi-major axis = 1.1143
Eccentricity = 0.07296
Inclination = $65°4$
t - in year days

These predictions supersede those previously furnished. As soon as significant departure fro this ephemeris is observed, new predictions will be sent.

CROSSINGS OF 40 DEGREES - SATELLITE 1957 BETA
PATH ANGLE = 30.665

SOUTH-NORTH			NORTH-SOUTH			SOUTH-NORTH			NORTH-SOUTH		
TIME (UT)	LONG. (W)	HT. (Mi)	TIME (UT)	LONG. (W)	HT. (Mi)	TIME (UT)	LONG. (W)	HT. (Mi)	TIME (UT)	LONG. (W)	HT. (Mi)
	January 30, 1958						January 31, 1958				
00 15	236.2	137	00 38	107.2	485	00 56	250.3	137	01 19	121.3	484
01 54	261.2	137	02 17	132.2	485	02 34	275.2	137	02 57	146.2	484
03 33	286.1	137	03 56	157.1	485	04 13	300.1	137	04 36	171.1	484
05 12	311.1	137	05 35	182.1	485	05 52	325.1	137	06 15	196.1	484
06 50	366.0	137	07 13	207.0	485	07 30	350.0	137	07 53	221.0	484
08 29	00.9	137	08 52	232.0	484	09 09	14.9	137	09 32	245.9	484
10 08	25.9	137	10 31	256.9	484	10 47	39.8	137	11 11	270.8	484
11 46	50.8	137	12 09	281.8	484	12 26	64.7	137	12 49	295.8	484
13 25	75.8	137	13 48	306.8	484	14 05	89.7	137	14 28	320.7	484
15 04	100.7	137	15 27	331.7	484	15 43	114.6	137	16 06	345.6	484
16 42	125.6	137	17 05	356.6	484	17 22	139.5	137	17 45	10.5	484
18 21	150.6	137	18 44	21.6	484	19 00	164.4	137	19 24	35.4	483
20 00	175.5	137	20 23	46.5	484	20 39	189.3	137	21 02	60.3	483
21 38	200.4	137	22 01	71.4	484	22 18	214.2	137	22 41	85.2	483
23 17	225.4	137	23 40	96.4	484	23 56	239.1	137	24 19	110.2	483

Predictions for daily passages of 1957 beta (Sputnik II) based on information sent in by Moonwatch teams. (Used by permission)

Chapter 2

Observing the Satellites

LOCATING A SATELLITE

Whether we can see a satellite is largely a matter of where we live and what the orbit is. The shivering scientists who took part in operation Deep Freeze probably saw the Russian Sputniks more often than anyone else in the world, or could have except for the raging blizzards of the polar region. The orbits of these satellites carried them fairly close to the polar regions on every trip. On the other hand, nobody in that region ever saw an American satellite. Let's look at the reason for this a little more closely.

If a satellite is launched with an inclination of 35°, it moves back and forth across the equator between latitudes 35° north and 35° south. It would never come north of a line running through Charlotte, North Carolina, or south of another line passing through the Cape of Good Hope. If it happened to be at apogee at the northernmost part of its orbit, people at the latitude of Buffalo, New York, would see it low in the sky. But if it were at perigee, it would never appear above the horizon.

Because the plane of a satellite's orbit must pass through the center of the earth, a satellite launched from any point on the earth can never have an inclination *less* than the latitude of its launching site. The reason for this may be seen if we stretch an elastic band around a small globe, using any point on the globe as a theoretical launching area. The elastic band must be placed so that it follows a great circle on the surface of the globe (a great circle on a sphere is the imaginary line formed on the surface of a sphere where it meets a plane passing through the center of the sphere). Placed in this way, the elastic band can be made to assume any angle with the equator *greater* than the latitude of the launching site, but never less.

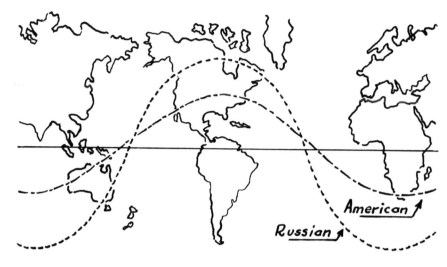

American ↗

Russian ↗

Orbits of the satellites.

This means that a satellite launched from a point 35° north of the equator *must* pass over some point an equal distance south of the equator.

But it should be added that this applies only to satellites that receive no additional thrust after they are placed in orbit. If some way is worked out to supply more power after the orbit is attained, the initial orbit can be changed to any new one desired. No satellite yet launched, however, has this extra power supply.

The chances of seeing a satellite also depend on its size and height. Even though we never see the satellite itself, but only the light reflected from it, it still must have enough surface area to reflect sufficient light to be picked up by the human eye. Explorer I is a small satellite with a small surface area. Few people have seen it for this reason alone. Furthermore, its orbit is a large one, 1,600 miles at apogee and 200 at perigee, and this adds another difficulty. The intensity of light diminishes according to the square of the distance from its source. At 1,600 miles, for this reason, the light reaching the earth from its surface is only 1/64 of that reflected at 200 miles.

Now let's assume that the orbit and other conditions are such that a satellite can be seen from the spot where we happen to be. We saw earlier that predicting its appearance by mathematics involves difficulties many of us are not prepared to cope with. Fortunately, this problem has been attacked by people with more mathematical knowledge than we possess, and the result is a number of devices by which we can predict a satellite's local appearance. There are at least three different types of these devices, each of which will tell us where to look for a satellite provided we are able to supply several pieces of basic information. We must obtain the location of some place over which it will pass, its direction of travel, the probable time of its passage, and its height. This information is usually carried in newspapers or broadcast by radio when a satellite is due, based upon predictions issued by the Smithsonian Astrophysical Observatory.

SATELLITE FINDERS BASED ON MAPS

An excellent example of this kind of satellite finder was first issued by the National Geographic Society in December, 1957, and was fully described in the National Geographic Magazine for that month. It consists of two parts, a special 42-by-29-inch map of the United States, and a scale stamped on a plastic overlay to be used with the map. The scale is made up of a number of lines representing varying heights at which satellites may be flying, and each of these lines is divided into units representing the altitude, or distance in degrees, at which the satellite may be seen above the horizon. A base line is drawn on the map corresponding to the direction of expected travel of the satellite, usually between two cities over which it will pass. Then we draw a perpendicular from where we live—in this case it is Toledo, Ohio—to the base line. This is the direction in which we shall look for the satellite.

Now we place the plastic overlay on the map so that the column representing the expected height of the satellite falls on the perpendicular, with the 90° mark over Toledo. At the point where the column crosses the base line, we find a number indicating the angle of altitude, or height above the horizon, at which the satellite will be flying at its highest point. This finder kit is very simple to use and may be purchased directly from the National Geographic Society for two dollars.

THE PLANISPHERE TYPE OF FINDER

These devices look like the planispheres, or star finders, usually sold at planetariums. One of the best is published by the Library of Science for $1.95 and was designed by Dr. K. L. Franklin of the Hayden Planetarium. It consists of three parts: a clock-faced base card over which is mounted two disks, the lower a map of the world and the upper an acetate sheet upon which may be drawn the orbit of the satellite. The disk containing the world map is rotated until the proper time zone printed on its outside edge coincides with the expected time of passage on the clock face of the

The Library of Science Satellite Pathfinder. (Used by permission of the Library of Science; Millbrook School Photo Service photograph)

base card. The acetate disk is then rotated until the orbit line for the satellite falls over the location of the observer. This orbit line traces the path of the satellite for the whole Northern Hemisphere. Complete and detailed instructions are included with the finder; and, once they are mastered, the device is a very useful one.

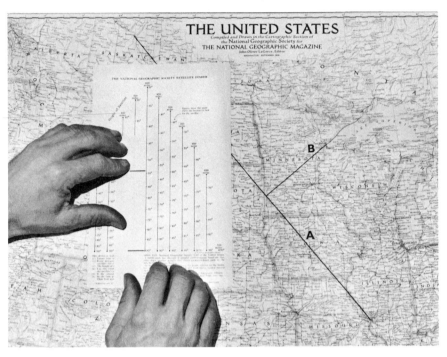

Plastic overlay and map used with the National Geographic Society Satellite Finder. (Copyright National Geographic Society)

The Finder in use. Here it is used to locate a satellite position from Toledo, Ohio. (Millbrook School Photo Service photograph)

Graph type of finder. (Used by permission of Jack W. Slowey; Millbrook School Photo Service photograph)

THE GRAPH TYPE OF FINDER

Although most of us tend to shy away from graphs, chiefly because they look complicated and partly because some of us have bitter memories of exposure to mathematics in school, the satellite finders that make use of graphs are very simple and accurate to use. A particularly useful example is shown here. If the reader has the courage to tackle it, he will find it is not as terrifying as it looks. It was designed by Mr. Jack W. Slowey, physicist on the staff of the Smithsonian Astrophysical Observatory, especially for the use of Moonwatch teams.

The four main elements for finding satellites are listed on this graph. The horizontal straight lines represent the range, or actual distance, from the observer to the satellite along the observer's line of sight. The vertical straight lines show the elevation of the satellite above the horizon in degrees. The set of curved lines that sweep up to the right give the distance in degrees from the observer to the point on the earth where the satellite is directly overhead, or the sub-satellite point. Land distances can be readily converted to degrees, and vice versa, allowing 69 statute miles for one degree. Finally, the curved lines that sweep up to the left represent the perpendicular height of the satellite in miles above the surface of the earth. If any two of these four main factors is known, the other two may easily be found. Usually the two factors that are known about a satellite are its height and some point over which it will pass. The land distance from the observer to this point may be measured in degrees, using any good map of the United States, or measured in miles and then converted into degrees.

This insistence on measuring distance in degrees may seem somewhat strange, but it has a very simple explanation. Most of the reports issued on satellites do not state that it will pass over some point, such as Walla Walla, but say instead that it will cross the 39th parallel of latitude at 77° west longitude. If we consult the longitude scale at the top of a map and the latitude scale at the side, we see that these two lines cross at Washington, D.C. Now suppose we live in Memphis, Tennessee. If we measure the distance between Washington and Memphis with a pair of dividers and compare the spread in the dividers with the latitude scale on the side of the map opposite Memphis, we find the distance to be 11°. We never need to know how far it is in miles, for we will go directly to the satellite finder graph with the number of degrees.

HOW TO USE THE GRAPH

Let us assume that we live in Memphis, since that is the example already used, and that the satellite is to make a dawn passage over Washington at a height of 300 miles. We aren't particularly anxious to get up before dawn, but if the finder tells us we will get a good look at a satellite by doing so, we decide it will be worth the effort. So we find the curved line on the left of the graph marked 11° (the angular distance to Washington) and follow it up to the point where it crosses the oppositely curved line marked 300 miles. We now follow the vertical straight line from this point to the bottom of the scale, where we find that the satellite will be 15° above the horizon. We go back to the point, then follow the horizontal straight line to the left where we discover that, as the crow flies, the distance to the satellite will be 850 miles. Fifteen degrees above the horizon and 850 miles away sounds discouraging, since objects that low and that far away are hard to see under the best of conditions. But if the satellite is very bright, we might see it anyway. To get some information on this, we look at the scale on the extreme right-hand margin, which tells us that a 21-inch sphere at a height of 300 miles will have a magnitude of between 6.0 and 6.5. Furthermore, the scale applies to satellites passing directly overhead. Since the satellite is 850 miles away, it will be even less bright than the scale indicates. This is even more discouraging, for an object with a magnitude in this range cannot be seen with the naked eye. In the face of all this, we do not bother to set the alarm clock.

THE CIVIL AIR PATROL POSITION GRID

This is only one part of a system for disseminating up-to-the-minute information about satellites. In order to understand how the finder works we must look at the whole system. Its essential features consist of:

1. Special messages about satellites sent daily over

2. Short-wave radio transmitters operated by the Civil Air Patrol, based on

3. Predictions made by the Smithsonian Astrophysical Observatory, which are

4. Plotted on a special graph (grid) constructed for the purpose of a quick evaluation of the relative positions of observer and satellite.

The messages are sent in a simple code in which key information is converted into words or phrases.

1. *Satellite designation.* Each satellite is referred to by the year in which it was launched, followed by an appropriate Greek letter for the launching sequence of that year.

   EXAMPLES: Sputnik I rocket = 1957 alpha 1; satellite of
   Sputnik I = 1957 alpha 2; Sputnik II = 1957 beta;
   Explorer I = 1958 alpha; Vanguard I = 1958 beta.

   (See appendix for the Greek alphabet).

2. *Observing conditions.*

   Condition Black: Satellite in earth's shadow and cannot be seen.

   Condition White: The background sky is too bright for an observer directly below the satellite.

   Condition Green: This is the transition zone, where the observer is in shadow and the satellite in sunlight. It is the most favorable condition for observation.

   Condition Red: A self-luminous satellite, such as Sputnik II just before its final plunge.

3. *Inclination.* The angle between the plane of the orbit and the plane of the equator.

4. *Period.* The time for one complete revolution of the satellite.

5. *40th parallel intercept.* The longitude of the point where the satellite crosses the 40th parallel of latitude. Applies to satellites which have a north-south orbit.

6. *Vertex.* The longitude of the northernmost point in the orbit if the satellite does not cross the 40th parallel.

7. *Longitude notation.* Given in degrees and 10ths. Always a four-digit number. Examples: 0783 = 78.3° west; 1214 = 121.4° west.

8. *Latitude notation.* Given in degrees and 10ths. Always a three-digit number. Example: 080 = 8.0 north.

9. *Time.* Eastern Standard Time.

Perhaps the best way to see how the code works is to quote a sample message and its interpretation:

On 7 February earth satellite 1957 beta will be 148 statute miles high and condition green heading 031 degrees across the 40th parallel. 40th parallel intercept 0803 west at 0640 EST, leaving condition black latitude 080 north at 0635 EST, entering condition white latitude 440 north at 0645 EST.

or

On February 7th Sputnik II will be 148 statute (land) miles high and in favorable position to be seen. It will be heading to the northeast (031°) across the 40th parallel. It will cross the 40th parallel at longitude 80.3° west at 6:40 A.M., Eastern Standard Time. It will leave the shadow of the earth at latitude 8° north at 6:35 A.M., but by the time it arrives at the 44th parallel at 6:45 A.M. the sky will be too bright for it to be seen.

The Civil Air Patrol broadcasts satellite information on the following schedule:

Command Station (VP zero)		4275 KC	1900 EST
			2000 EST
			2100 EST

Rebroadcasts:

Northeast region	4585	KC	2030 EST
Middle East region	4467.5	KC	2030 EST
Southeast region	4467.5	KC	2030 EST
Great Lakes region	4507.5	KC	2030 EST
North Central region	2374	KC	2030 CST
Southwest region	4507.5	KC	2030 CST
Rocky Mountain region	4585	KC	2030 MST
Pacific region	4585	KC	2030 PST

These frequencies are too high for ordinary radio receivers, but they can be picked up very clearly on short-wave radios.

USING THE GRID SHEET

The plotting sheet (grid) shown here is constructed so the satellite is always assumed to go through the vertical line marked 0°. The position of the observer is plotted east or west of this line and on the proper latitude line. Again an example is the best way to show how it is used.

Let us assume that the point where the observer is stationed is at 77.1° west longitude and 38.0° north latitude. The message tells him the satellite will cross the 40th parallel at 80.3° west longitude, or near Morgantown, West Virginia. (We are translating the longitudes and latitudes into approximate locations to make it easier to follow the argument on a map, if the reader wishes to.)

The observer plots his position on the 38th parallel at a point 3.2° east of the 0° line (80.3 − 77.1 = 3.2). From this position he draws a line perpendicular to the nearest point on the line representing the path of the satellite. This perpendicular represents the direction he will look to see the satellite at its point of nearest approach (PNA), and also represents the distance to the sub-satellite point. Using the scale at the bottom of the chart, he finds this distance to be about 220 statute miles. Then, using the scale on the bottom of the chart at the left, he measures the distance in degrees. Using the value found (about 3.5° in this case), he enters the table of photo-track camera elevation (see appendix) with this figure and the height of the satellite (148 miles). The altitude of the satellite turns out to be about 31°.

HOW TO WATCH FOR SATELLITES

While this section applies to all satellite watchers, it is particularly directed toward those who prefer to do their watching without optical aid—and to be as comfortable as possible in the process.

Looking for artificial moons can be as enjoyable as we wish to make it if we take a few simple precautions; otherwise it may be a frustrating and uncomfortable experience. If the time of passage has been predicted, we go outside at least a half hour beforehand. This may seem as silly as arriving a half hour early to catch a train, but there are several good reasons for it. In the first place, newspaper and radio reports rarely give an exact time for a satellite passage, not because of inaccurate reporting, but because any report of a satellite passage is an estimate and not a precise figure. As more information about satellites is gathered, reports about their times of passages will undoubtedly become more precise. In the meantime, let's be on the scene early.

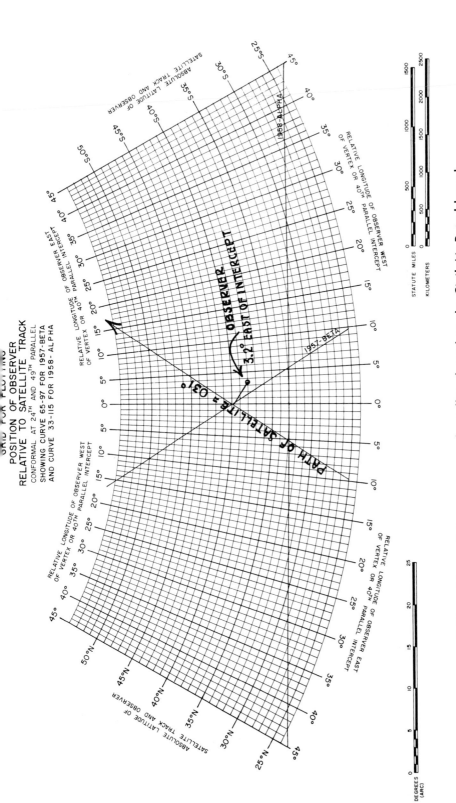

Grid used to predict appearance of satellites based on the Civil Air Patrol broadcasts. (Used by permission of the National Academy of Sciences)

The best reason for an early arrival is to accustom our eyes to the darkness. The human eye takes time to adjust itself to changing conditions of light and dark. In daylight the pupil of the eye contracts to a diameter of about 2 millimeters (1/12 inch), and at night expands to as much as 8 millimeters. More important, as far as vision is concerned, are the rod and cone cells which are part of the retina. The rods function chiefly for light perception, and the cones for color. It takes as much as half an hour for each type of cell to adapt itself for night vision, although this time varies for different people. A watch officer on a ship gives himself plenty of time to acquire night vision before he goes on the bridge, and satellite watchers will show wisdom if they do likewise.

Getting to the observation site early also gives us some time to look over the prominent constellations of the sky so we can reconstruct the passage of the satellite after it has gone by. Half the fun of satellite watching is to review the experience later. Those who don't know the constellations will find this a good time to learn a few of them. But let's not take along star charts, star finders, or anything else for which we need flashlights. We have adjusted our eyes to the darkness by this time and we do not want to spoil that adjustment by shining bright lights. Instead, memorize various star patterns; then look them up on a chart after the satellite has passed. It goes without saying that we shall try to find an observing site where there are no obstructions to the view and, above all, where there are no bright lights.

Once we arrive at the site we make ourselves as comfortable as possible. We have probably already taken the precaution of dressing warmly, for even a summer night becomes chilly when one is sitting or standing still. If the expected passage is to take place before dawn that extra sweater is even more important.

The most useful piece of apparatus we can take with us is a folding deck chair. When a satellite is to pass overhead, standing with the head tipped back is about the surest way to make us sorry, the next day, that we ever became interested in satellites. Looking at the sky from a reclining position gives the eyes the best possible chance to function efficiently. Since we already know the direction from which the satellite will come, we place the chair accordingly, climb in it (preferably with a blanket), and start observing. But let's be very sure we remember the direction from which the satellite is coming, for seeing one just as it disappears because we have placed our back to its arrival is an awful letdown.

While we are waiting, we use the sky as a training ground for the eyes. The area of most acute vision is a tiny spot at the back of the eye called the *fovea centralis*; but, curiously enough, this area is not the most sensitive to faintly illuminated objects. A dim object is best seen from "out of the corner of the eye." This can be demonstrated by looking at the faintest star we can find. If we look slightly away from the star, we can see it more clearly than if we stare at it. At this point in our preparations it is best not to look at bright stars, at least directly; and, if the moon is out, we ignore its beauties.

If the time is now approaching when the satellite is due, we start looking for motion in the area of the sky where we think it will appear. We try to make ourselves conscious of the fact that the stars are standing still; for, if we can do this, any movement among them becomes instantly apparent. The satellite will not come rushing across the sky; it moves much more slowly than we expect if this is the first one we have seen.

Once we have found it, we attempt to estimate its brightness in comparison with nearby stars, and we notice particularly whether this brightness varies during its passage across the sky. It is also worth while trying to time its passage between any two bright stars that lie along its track. (A simple way to count seconds is the old "thousand-one, thousand-two," and so on method). Afterward it is fun to look up the two stars on a chart and figure out the speed of the satellite in degrees per second. We also look for color in the satellite and notice whether the color changes as it passes across the sky. But the chances are that we will forget all the things we intended to look for and will stare, wide-eyed and unthinking, overcome with the beauty and majesty of the tiny object as it sails serenely across the heavens so far above us.

MAGNITUDE

Because one of the characteristics we look for in a satellite is brightness, or magnitude, we might stop for a moment to see how this word is used in astronomy. The twenty brightest stars in the heavens are of the first magnitude or brighter. From this point they become progressively less bright, and when they get down to the 6th magnitude, we need a telescope or binoculars to see them at all. Roughly speaking, a 1st-magnitude star is 2½ times brighter than one of the 2nd magnitude, and the same factor holds all the way down the line. By the time we get down to the 6th magnitude we find stars that are only 1/100 as bright as their 1st-magnitude cousins. A good pair of binoculars will bring out stars as dim as the 10th magnitude, and the great 200-inch telescope at Mt. Palomar searches out objects as dim as the 24th.

On the other end of the scale, stars *brighter* than first magnitude are given zero or negative numbers to indicate their brightness. Thus the winter star Sirius is -1.6, Venus at her brightest is -4.0, and the sun is -27. Possibly a better idea of magnitudes can be obtained from examples at this end of the scale. When we look at the summer sky, one of the most familiar star groups is the great right-angle triangle made up of the bright stars Vega, Altair, and Deneb. Vega, the star at the right angle and the brightest of the three, has a magnitude of 0.1. The other two are typical 1st-magnitude stars. The next step down on the scale is represented by Polaris, the North Star, which is of the second magnitude. The four stars in the bowl of the Little Dipper (whose handle ends in the North Star) are 2nd, 3rd, 4th, and 5th magnitudes, respectively, as shown in the diagram. If we turn now to the Big Dipper and follow its handle to the place where it bends, very sharp eyes will see a tiny star (Alcor) located just above Mizar, the star at the crook in the handle. This little star is about as difficult to see as one of the 6th magnitude and makes a good test for the sharpness of our eyesight.

Star magnitudes.

Satellites appear brightest when they are in a band of the sky ranging from directly overhead down to about 45° above the horizon. Below this point they become less distinct since they must be seen through heavier layers of atmosphere. Their visibility below 15° is completely unpredictable, for this is the area of haze and smog that surrounds most cities.

Finally, the size of a satellite, its surface area, and its shape are also contributors to its brightness. A satellite with a diameter of 60 inches will be approximately four times as bright as one of 30 inches, while one of 120 inches diameter will be 16 times as bright. This was strikingly brought out by the third-stage rocket of the first Sputnik, whose brightness was unbelievable compared to the satellite itself. The latter was seen only a few times, while the former was observed by hundreds of thousands of excited watchers.

WATCHING FOR NEW SATELLITES

Hunting for a new satellite is even more exciting than looking at those which have been in the heavens for some time and whose orbits have been worked out. This involves much longer observing periods, of course, since the exact time of passage will not be known. Just where it will appear in the sky, too, will be guesswork. The only thing we may be sure of will be its approximate brightness, since the size of the satellite is usually announced with its launching. Satellites of the Explorer type are faint, ranging from magnitude 5 (just within naked eye limits) to 8 or 9. On the other hand, those which include some part of the launching vehicle, such as the Sputniks, are often as bright as first magnitude.

This information about brightness helps us greatly in determining the length of the observing period. There is little use in looking for a dim object just before sunrise or immediately after sunset, since the sky must be completely dark if we are to see it. So we make use of what is called *duration of twilight* to estimate the time we should spend at the observation post.

Most of us think of twilight as an indefinite period in the early morning or evening. Actually there are three definitions of this period, each marked by a specific gradation of darkness.

Civil twilight is a half-hour period just before sunrise or after sunset when the sun is less than 6° below the horizon. The sky is relatively bright during that time, especially in the direction of the sun; and only very bright satellites may be seen. We shall waste our time looking for others. *Nautical* twilight is the period when the sun is less than 12° below the horizon; it includes civil twilight as well, but its last half hour is a favorable interval for the observation of both faint and bright satellites. *Astronomical* twilight includes both civil and nautical, but extends a half hour beyond or until the sun is 18° below the horizon. During its final half hour we may hope to see the faintest satellites. Indeed, this is the only time some of them can be seen with the naked eye.

Each of these periods lasts, on the average, for half an hour. But their duration varies with the time of year and with geographical location. In the tropics, astronomical twilight lasts for only an hour at any time of the year, while at latitudes north of 60° it continues all night from May to September. Because of the angle at which the earth is inclined, in polar regions the sun is never very far below or above the horizon. In middle latitudes (40° to 60°), twilight may last as long as 2½ hours in the summer. Fortunately, the duration of twilight for any day of the year is included in astronomical tables. We have included excerpts from these in the appendix for exact lengths of the periods during which we will want to watch on any specific morning or evening.

While the duration of twilight gives us a measuring stick by which we can judge our chances of seeing a new satellite, common sense is just about as useful. In the evening, we wait until we can see stars of the magnitude we expect the satellite to be, and start looking. In the morning, we begin our search between an hour and a half and two hours before the time the newspaper tells us the sun will come up, and quit when we lose sight of our guide stars. These general statements apply only to naked-eye observing, however; for we shall see later that they must be modified a little if we use telescopes or binoculars.

One great help in picking up a newly launched satellite is that its radio is usually still working. If we are fortunate enough to have a radio with a 10-meter band, we can pick up the transmissions of Russian satellites on 20.005 or 40.002 megacycles. Signals coming from satellites can usually be heard several minutes before the satellite passes the meridian (the north-south line in the sky directly overhead of our observing site), and this gives us time to get ready to observe it visually. American radio transmissions are more of a problem, however, for they broadcast on 108.00 and 108.03 megacycles; and radios capable of picking up these frequencies are hard to acquire.

At best radio detection is a somewhat tricky business, for satellite radio signals have a bad habit of bouncing around so that receivers do not pick them up. If too much dependence is placed on radio signals as a warning device, the satellite may be missed altogether. Yet in at least one case, the use of radio equipment not only warned watchers that a satellite was coming, but actually located it for them. The Moonwatch team at Manhattan, Kansas, located the first American satellite when one of the members of the team sighted along the directional antenna of his receiver and found Explorer I within a degree of where the antenna was pointing.

Chapter **3**

Using Binoculars

WHY WE NEED OPTICAL HELP

The first two American satellites, Explorer I and Vanguard I, will be aloft for some years to come and there will be many opportunities to see them, even though their small size and large orbits make them difficult to find. When they are closest to us they are barely visible to the naked eye, even under the most favorable atmospheric conditions. For a really good look, we must use an optical aid. A dash to the attic to find our old opera glasses or spyglass is not going to help much, since this equipment is inadequate. What, then, do we need?

The sky covers much more space than most of us realize. From horizon to horizon it stretches about 180°. This sweep becomes all the larger when we consider that the full moon takes up only half a degree, and the seemingly large distance between the pointers of the Big Dipper is only five degrees. Consequently, our optical device must cover as much sky as possible or, to use the optical term, must have a wide *field of view*. The smaller the field, of course, the easier it is for the satellite to elude our hunt.

For this reason opera glasses and simple telescopes are nearly useless: they do not have a large enough field of view. They are based on the Galilean design (so called because Galileo himself invented it). They give a clear, upright image and are useful for almost everything except satellite watching. Opera glasses and simple telescopes make use of what is called a *negative eyepiece* which, in simple terms, is one that cannot be used as an ordinary magnifying glass, for it produces an image within the eyepiece itself. All optical instruments with this kind of eyepiece have a small field of view, usually less than 5°. They include, along with opera glasses and

folding telescopes, the double-barreled instruments called field glasses
These have no prisms, in contrast to binoculars, and are focused by a tele
scoping arrangement of the barrels of the instrument.

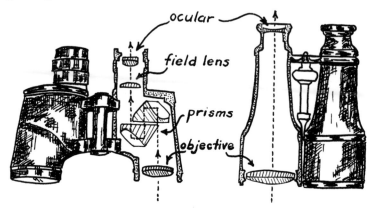

Binoculars (left) and field glasses. Both instruments pictured here give
bright, clear images. The prisms in binoculars "fold" the path of the
light and thus produce a more compact instrument. The only disadvantage of field glasses is their small field of view.

TESTING FOR FIELD OF VIEW

A good field of view for a satellite telescope, for reasons discussed
later, is about 12°, and we shall accept this figure as a fundamental criterion.
We can test any instrument on the stars themselves to see how well they
meet this criterion. The Big Dipper makes a good standard. The pointers
cover an area of 5°, an absolute minimum for any instrument used for
satellite watching. The two stars at the bottom of the bowl represent a
spread of 9½°, and from the inner edge of the bowl to the end of the handle
there is a space of 15°.

Most of the instruments we test will disappoint us. Telescopes, especially under high power, have a very small field of view (only half a degree);
and even 7 × 50 binoculars cover an area of only about 7°. On the other
hand, there are wide-angle binoculars that have fields of over 9°. These
are still a little limited for satellite viewing, but they can be expected to
give results.

Many of us do not wish to go to the trouble of buying or making a
telescope especially designed for satellite watching. But we may want to
acquire a good pair of binoculars, since they can be used for other purposes
as well.

Since telescopes and binoculars operate according to the same optical principles (binoculars, as their name indicates, are only a pair of short elescopes used together), let us study this diagram of a telescope. We must pause a moment to learn some basic optics, but it will help us in buying a good pair of binoculars.

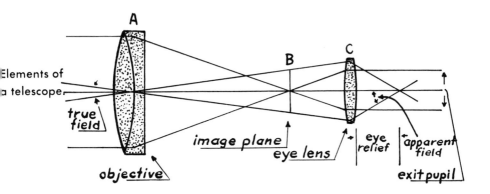

The *objective lens* (A) focuses light rays coming from an object and produces an image at area B, called the *image plane*. The *eyepiece* (C) enlarges this image so that it can be examined by the eye. The size of the beam of light emerging from the eyepiece is called the *exit pupil,* and the distance from the eyepiece to where the image is sharpest is known as *eye relief.*

The distances of the objective lens and the eyepiece from the image plane are called *focal lengths,* since each focuses on the same point. We can also express this as the distance from a lens to the point where parallel rays passing through it are bent to a sharp focus. This definition applies to a single lens. When we wish to refer to the focal length of a *lens system,* such as the eyepiece, which is made up of several lenses working as a single unit, we call it the *equivalent focal length.* Here the focal length of a simple lens is equal to the system in question.

The *magnification* of telescopes or binoculars is equal to the focal length of the objective divided by that of the eyepiece. It is a popular belief that magnification is an all-important attribute of a pair of binoculars. Actually it is the last factor we should consider. Magnification, often referred to as *power,* is simply the number of times larger, or closer, an object looks through an optical instrument than with the naked eye. It is important if we wish to examine a small object in detail, such as one of the smaller moon craters, but it always reduces the field of view and usually cuts down

35

on the brightness of the object. Furthermore, the greater the magnification, the harder it is to use the instrument without some kind of support, because the least motion causes the image to dance in the field. This is a great disadvantage if we are trying to follow a faint, rapidly moving satellite. It often means we will lose it altogether.

The main function of the objective lens is to collect light, provided that the remainder of the system is arranged so that its full diameter is used. The amount of light collected determines the brightness of the image formed, an aspect at least as important in any binoculars as the magnification. This is why bird watchers like binoculars with big objectives: they can see the color of the bird clearly, even if he is in shadow. Mathematically, the brightness of the image is proportional to the *square* of the diameter, which means that a 50-mm objective will produce an image four times as bright as one of 25 mm, and approximately twice as bright as one of 35 mm.

At this point we might digress a bit to talk about coated lenses. When light strikes the surface of a lens, about 95 per cent of it passes through. The remaining 5 per cent is reflected and thus lost to the viewer. This represents a serious loss of brightness in the image if, as in the case of binoculars, the light must pass through at least ten surfaces, losing 5 per cent at each. However, if the lenses are coated with a material such as magnesium fluoride, the reflection is cut to a minimum, and the light loss is reduced to only ½ per cent per surface.

Field of view in telescopes—that is, the *area* that they cover in contrast to the difference in apparent size or closeness of an object in the area—depends on the eyepiece. The objective alone has a considerable field and forms an image of this area at the focal plane. If the eyepiece has a field (called the *apparent field*) sufficient to take in the whole image at the focal plane, the telescope as a whole will have the same field as the objective. A wide-angle eyepiece will therefore produce a wide field in the telescope. This can be found mathematically by dividing the apparent field of the eyepiece by the magnification of the telescope. Thus a 40° eyepiece set in an 8-power telescope will give the whole telescope a field of 5°; if a 68° eyepiece is put in a telescope of this power, the field will be 8.5°. There are many misleading claims about this aspect of telescopes and binoculars. One of them is the statement that a wide objective produces a wide field. This is untrue for, as we said above, it is the eyepiece that is important in this respect.

The *exit pupil* is also an important factor in telescopes because it determines the diameter of the beam of light that actually enters the eye. A telescope can accommodate a beam of light as wide as the diameter of its objective. The beam emerging from the telescope, however, will be considerably smaller. We can calculate the diameter of this emergent beam

A wide-angle Erfle eyepiece (left) compared to the eyepiece of 7×50 binoculars. Both are oriented on the same spot. Notice the way the Erfle picks up the window on the side of the room where the photo was taken. (Millbrook School Photo Service)

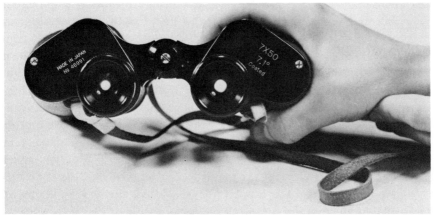

Exit pupil. The eyepiece on the right is not focused, which makes the exit pupil appear slightly larger. (Millbrook School Photo Service)

by dividing the aperture of the objective (the diameter of the lens reduced by the supports required for mounting it) by the magnification.

The pupil of the eye varies from about 2 mm during the day to 8 mm at night. If the exit pupil of the telescope is too small, the eye cannot be utilized to its full seeing power; if it is too large, some of the light cannot enter the eye. Binoculars will give maximum performance for nighttime use if the exit pupil corresponds to the nighttime size of the pupil of the eye. We can make a rough estimate of the size of the exit pupil by holding the instrument at arm's length, with the objective lens directed toward a bright window or other source of light. The bright spot now seen in the center of the eyepiece is the exit pupil. If the spot is about ⅜ inch, the instrument will perform well at night.

Also of much importance is *eye relief*. If we find it necessary to place the eye so close to the eyepiece that lashes get in the way, the eye relief is too short. One notices this with microscopes at high power; in telescopes or binoculars short eye relief is intolerable since it makes it difficult to find the exit pupil in the dark and is fatiguing as well. Any situation in which the eye feels "crowded" always produces strain. If we wear glasses good eye relief is especially important. It must, at a minimum, be equal to the normal distance of the glasses from the eye, about ⅜ inch. Values ranging from this to 1 inch are most comfortable. If the value is low, the glasses must be removed, which means readjusting our vision to a new set of conditions every time we use the binoculars. Since we need top vision for chasing satellites, no last-minute readjustment is tolerable. The mathematics of eye relief is more complicated than that of magnification or exit pupil. We must delve into optics further to determine eye relief exactly, so we say here only that it is usually a little less than the focal length of the eyepiece and turn to the appendix for the exact means of determining it.

BINOCULAR CHECK LIST

We can sum up this information in the form of a check list to use when buying binoculars. This list applies, for the most part, to binoculars purchased for satellite watching, but it is a helpful check when buying them for any use.

1. The two numbers usually applied in classifying binoculars give their magnifying power and the diameter of the objective lens. Thus 6×30, for example, means they are 6 power (magnify 6 times) and have an objective diameter of 30 mm (to change millimeters into inches, multiply by 0.04). If you plan to use your binoculars to watch birds as well as satellites, the larger the objective diameter the better, since the image will be brighter (see table below). But watch out for large magnifications—they are usually more trouble than they are worth. Remember that binoculars over 10 power must be tripod-held, since the hands simply cannot hold them steadily enough for good vision.

2. Look for a wide field of view. If you cannot test the binoculars on a star field, information about the size of field is usually stamped on the barrel of the instrument beside the right-hand eyepiece. If it says only "wide angle," ask for more specific information, such as the apparent field of the eyepiece. Knowing the magnification, you can then figure out the actual width of the field for yourself (apparent field of eyepiece, in degrees divided by magnification). You will be surprised how many instruments stamped "wide angle" do not qualify for this designation. Sometimes the field is given in degrees, but more often it is supplied by a statement such as 367 feet at 1,000 yards. This can be converted into degrees by the table here.

Size	Light Transmission	Field of View at 1000 Yds.	Degrees	Use
6×30	37	445 ft.	8	General purpose. Good for satellites. Easy on the eyes.
7×35	37	381 "	7	Excellent general purpose. Minimum field for satellites.
7×35	37	525 " (wide-angle)	10	Best for satellites.
7×50	75	381 "	7	Excellent for any purpose where bright field, detail, and color transmission desired.
8×30	21	330 "	6	Not recommended for satellites.
8×40	37	375 "	7	General purpose.
9×35	23	381 "	7 ⎫	These two not recommended for
10×50	37	375 "	7 ⎭	satellites. If used, must be tripod-held.

If we accept a light transmission value of 30 as acceptable, the 7×50 binoculars rate very high. In general, this size is the best all-purpose binoculars.

3. Check for an exit pupil that falls between 3 mm (⅛ inch) and 8 mm (about ⅜ inch). The closer to the upper limit, the better for night vision.

4. Check carefully for sharpness of image at the edge of the field. Poor functioning in this respect is called *spherical aberration*. At night it will make stars on the outer edges of the field appear as blobs or lines instead of sharp images. There is usually a small amount of spherical aberration in all binoculars; but, if the defect is pronounced, look for another pair.

5. Look for *chromatic aberration*. This means that the binoculars, instead of providing a colorless image, will surround it with colors of various hues. If this aberration is only barely evident when the binoculars are focused on some object—a twig, or a ball at the end of a flagpole—against a bright sky, it does no harm. But if it makes the twig look as though it were painted by Titian, the binoculars have a serious defect and are not worth buying.

6. Look for distortion, which is a tendency for square objects to become bent inward or outward on the edges of the field. A small amount is tolerable, but binoculars that transform a square into either a pincushion or a barrel should be avoided.

7. Look at the objective lens carefully. If there is any evidence of what looks like faint spider-webbing under the surface of the glass, it means that the bonding substance used to hold the elements of the lens together has come loose. This will get worse as the binoculars get older, and eventually becomes ruinous.

8. Ask about lens coatings. As we said earlier, coated lenses permit the passage of almost all the light that enters the objective. But this applies

Lens separation in a 7×50 binocular objective. The bonding material between the two glass surfaces has broken away, producing what looks like a fungus growth between them. (Millbrook School Photo Service)

7×50 individual-focus (left) compared with 7×35 center-focus binoculars. (Millbrook School Photo Service)

only if *all* surfaces are coated, not just the objective itself. Coated lenses have a bluish tinge when held at an angle to the light, but the presence of this color does not mean that the elements inside the binoculars are also coated. Unless we wish to dismantle the binoculars, we shall have to take the word of the manufacturer. All other things being equal, the more expensive the instrument, the more likely that all surfaces are adequately coated.

9. Center-focusing binoculars are easier to use than those in which each eyepiece has its own focus. However, unless both eyepieces move smoothly and evenly when the central focusing wheel is turned, this kind is useless, since it throws both eyepieces out of focus each time it is used. Furthermore, if there is any looseness in the sliding tubes that hold the eyepieces, dust and moisture get into the system. Individual-focus binoculars, on the other hand, are dust tight since the focusing works on threaded sleeves. For this reason, military binoculars are individually focused.

Nevertheless, many people prefer the center-focus kind chiefly because it is so easy to change focus from distant objects to those nearby. To adjust this type, turn the focusing wheel until the bridge that holds both eyepieces is as far out as it will go. Close the right eye and focus the left eyepiece by means of the center focusing wheel. Then, using its own focusing mechanism, focus the right eyepiece. Bend the hinge adjustment until the distance between eyepieces is such that each eye looks straight through its eyepiece. Note the reading on the scale at the center hinge and on the right eyepiece. By adjusting the binoculars to these readings at any future time, you will be ready to use them without refocusing. In the meantime, to shift focus from near to distant objects you need only to turn the central focusing wheel.

Individually focused eyepieces are adjusted in the same way, first extending both as far as possible, then focusing each in turn. Here, however, to adjust for different distances, you must refocus each eyepiece.

10. Finally, binoculars are like almost any other manufactured product: you get just about what you pay for. More money, up to a certain point, buys better optics, better machining of parts, better coatings, and better all-round performance. But if a comparatively inexpensive pair of binoculars satisfies the requirements listed above, it is probably a good buy.

USING BINOCULARS FOR THE SATELLITES

All the statements made in chapter 2 about observing satellites with the naked eye apply equally well when we use optical aids. The procedure is complicated by a telescope or binoculars, and some of the recommendations that we called desirable become requisites now.

It may seem unnecessarily obvious to discuss matters such as making sure that we have focused the binoculars properly and adjusted them to fit our eyes, but if we neglect to do this *before* we see the satellite, it is usually too late to make adjustments after it comes into view. These are important preparations, too, from the point of view of eyestrain, since improper adjustment of the distance between eyepieces makes one eye work against the other. The least deviation in focus for each eyepiece also produces this effect. It is not noticeable for short observing periods, but it builds up insidiously during long observations and the result is watering eyes or headache.

If we expect the satellite to be bright enough to be seen with the naked eye, we try to spot it without binoculars. This is because binoculars or telescopes confine our vision to the particular area they cover and inhibit our inherent ability to see out of the corner of the eye as we do when we use our eyes alone. We have already decided, by means of a satellite finder, approximately where and how high in the sky the satellite will appear. We plot this passage on a star map, pick out identifying constellations or bright stars that will identify the area in the sky itself, and begin our search.

When the satellite appears, we are careful not to take our eyes from it. We slide the binoculars up until they intercept the line of sight. (Practice this movement beforehand on a star or an airplane.) If we do this quickly enough, we never really lose sight of the speeding satellite in the very short interval between naked-eye and optical observation. Thus we can follow it across the sky without interruption. This is a great advantage in observing all the details of a satellite passage, for uninterrupted vision means we obtain a better impression of minute changes in color and brightness. We are also able to spot its apparent distance from identifying stars in the background, a tremendous help when we plot its passage afterward.

However, the real advantage of binoculars is in finding satellites too faint to be seen with the naked eye. This, of course, requires the continuous use of the binoculars from the beginning to the end of the observing period, and we must take every possible precaution to avoid the kind of strain that makes our efforts ineffective. For example, we never stand while we are looking at the sky with binoculars. Tipping the head back to look overhead is made even more tiresome by holding binoculars to the eyes. Use a deck chair or an ordinary chair if it has a back high enough to support the head. This will not only make observing easier and more pleasant but be a safeguard against eyestrain, since the binoculars can be held more easily at the proper angle to the eyes.

Another way to make observing easier is to sit at a very high table so the elbows, resting on the table top, make a natural support for the binoculars. It is astonishing how heavy an instrument weighing only a few ounces can become after a while. Use of a table limits movement, but usually not enough to interfere with the coverage of the area in which we expect to see the satellite. Once we spot it, the elbows are lifted to permit more freedom of motion.

MAKING A BINOCULAR SUPPORT

If the binoculars are high powered—10 power or over—they must be used with a tripod. Human muscles are simply not steady enough to keep an optical instrument from wavering a little, and the more high-powered the instrument, the more motion in the field a small waver will produce.

It is easy to build an inexpensive mount which will eliminate "dancing." The binoculars are opened to the point where they fit the eyes most comfortably, and the distance between the inside edges of each barrel is measured. A piece of hardwood (oak, if you can find it), 1 inch thick and 4 inches long, is cut wide enough to fit this opening. Drill a hole, slightly larger than the pin that holds the binoculars together, 1 inch from the end of the wood, and then saw across the hole. The two crescents thus produced are lined with felt, and the pieces of felt are fitted on the pin and screwed together, after you drill holes so the wood will not split. A piece of ⅝-inch dowel is cut to make a joint as shown in the diagram, using a ¼-inch bolt and wing nut as a tightening device. One end is inserted into the binocular holder and the other into an 8-inch piece of 2 by 2, after holes have been drilled to receive them. The dowel goes all the way through the 2 by 2, and is kept from slipping by a washer and pin. This should fit snugly in the 2 by 2, but not so tightly that it cannot be removed, since we may want to pick the binoculars up after the satellite is sighted. The dowel turns freely from side to side so the binoculars can sweep back and forth; up and down motion is accomplished by the joint.

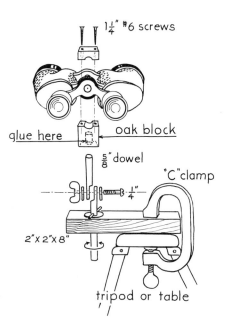

A simple
binocular
support.

The 2 by 2 is clamped on the head of a tripod or on a table with an ordinary "C" clamp. Most war surplus dealers have inexpensive tripods; the remainder of the items cost very little; and the whole arrangement, while crude, is well worth the money. It will work in almost any position except directly overhead, which is why we made it so we can pick it up if the path of the satellite swings high.

We set up the tripod, carefully focus the binoculars for faint stars, and adjust the whole apparatus to the most comfortable position for seeing. If the satellite finder has been properly used, the area we must cover will be a square section of the sky approximately 20° on a side. We sweep slowly across this section of the sky, moving the binoculars slowly up and down as we go. We emphasize the word *slowly*, which means just enough motion to make the stars appear in the field without streaking, that is, so they do not leave a trail of light behind them. It is important to avoid letting the eyes linger on bright stars or planets; and, above all, do not look at the moon. A few seconds of moonlight, even at the quarter, will impair our sight for as long as five minutes, during which time the satellite may sail by, completely undetected.

If the satellite is very bright, we can watch it with the naked eye for a few moments. But, if it is dim, trying to follow it without binoculars means we shall inevitably lose sight of it. Under these circumstances the satellite will be almost impossible to find again, since its motion in the binoculars, compared with that to the naked eye, is very hard to judge. This is because its apparent rate of motion in the binoculars is much greater than it appears to be to the naked eye, and we invariably look too far ahead or behind its true position.

Using a binocular support. (Millbrook School Photo Service)

Chapter 4

Using a Telescope

Chasing a satellite across the sky with a good telescope is a thrilling experience, for this is the clearest view we shall ever have of one of these elusive objects. We gain a very realistic impression of the speed of the satellite when we see it move against the countless background stars springing to view in the powerful glass. It looks larger and brighter, and, in its purposeful movement, seems startlingly man-made, not just a casual visitor from outer space. With the aid of a telescope we actually feel ourselves part of the satellite instead of only a watcher.

Using a high-powered telescope to follow a satellite is difficult, but finding the object in the first place is even more difficult. Telescopes are high-powered instruments compared to binoculars; they have a narrow field of view and thus cover only a small section of the sky. They are usually too heavy to be held by hand and must be supported by a mounting, which cuts down on their freedom of motion. For these reasons telescopes are held in low esteem by satellite watchers.

MOUNTING

We can overcome some of the difficulties if we are willing to take a few extra precautions and a little more trouble in preparing to look for the satellite. First we must make sure that the instrument is properly mounted and that we understand how the mounting works. There are two types of mountings commonly used for telescopes, the altazimuth and the equatorial.

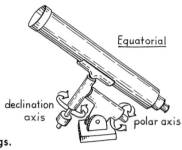

Equatorial

declination
axis

polar axis

Types of telescope mountings.

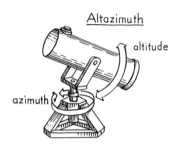

Altazimuth

altitude

azimuth

The *altazimuth* works exactly as its name indicates—in altitude (height) and in azimuth (lateral direction). The altitude axis of the mounting permits the telescope to move up or down, and the azimuth axis allows sideways motion. These two axes are set at right angles to each other as shown in the diagram, and a combination of the two motions makes movement possible in any direction. The mounting must be set on a high tripod or other support to make room for the telescope to move to a vertical position in case a satellite should pass directly overhead. The whole device must be solidly constructed, free to move easily in any direction without vibration. Following a satellite with such a device takes skill. To move any instrument in two directions at the same time is a difficult operation in itself, but to do it skillfully enough to follow a speeding object across the sky is more art than science.

Unfortunately for satellite watchers, not all telescopes have altazimuth mounts. Those used primarily for astronomical purposes have another type of mounting—the *equatorial*. This is like the altazimuth in that it has two axes perpendicular to each other, but unlike it in that one of the axes is tipped so it is parallel with a line through the poles of the earth. The amount of tipping is always equal to the latitude of the observer, varying from no inclination at the equator to 90° at the poles. This arrangement makes it possible to follow a star by moving the telescope only around the main, or polar, axis; but it must be moved around both axes to follow a satellite. The tipping of the whole system makes it awkward to use and we must put in

46

considerable practice before we can follow a moving object with any confidence. The best way to become skillful in this respect is to follow airplanes, starting with relatively slow-moving airliners and working up to jet planes. Anyone who can follow a low-flying jet plane with either an equatorial or altazimuth mounted telescope can follow a satellite without trouble.

LOCATING A SATELLITE

Having learned how to keep up with a satellite, there remains the more fundamental problem of how to locate it in the first place. Depending upon the magnification used, a telescope may have a field of view as small as half a degree—about the size of the full moon. To find a satellite with an instrument covering so small an area makes looking for a needle in a haystack seem easy. However, there are ways to overcome the difficulty. One possibility is to use binoculars and telescopes as a team. When the satellite appears in the wider-field binoculars, the telescope can be trained to the same area. Another and more certain method is to mount a small wide-field telescope on the larger one so their fields of view coincide. When the satellite appears in the center of the field of the wide-field telescope, it will also appear in the other one, and the observer quickly shifts his gaze to the other eyepiece. From this point on, the only limiting factor is his skill in following it.

This is a recommended technique, although often overlooked. A few Moonwatch teams have employed it successfully as a supplementary method to the standard way of following satellites. It is a good aid to celestial photography.

In spite of their clarity of view, few satellite watchers use large telescopes, partly because of their operating difficulties, but mostly because a good telescope is expensive. Many viewers, on the other hand, find binoculars difficult because, no matter what aids are adopted, they are tiresome to use for long periods of time.

THE MOONWATCH TELESCOPE

A small, wide-field instrument that can be used in comfort is a good compromise between the advantages and disadvantages of telescopes and binoculars. This instrument is already in wide use as the Moonwatch telescope, many of them constructed by the people who use them. They can also be purchased from commercial sources, and the number of optical supply houses that produce them is constantly increasing. These are good, practical telescopes, ideally suited for satellite purposes, but unfortunately they are quite expensive. Most of us do not want to invest in a one-purpose optical instrument.

Why not make them ourselves? No great mechanical skill is required, the basic optical knowledge can be acquired quickly, and the size of the cash outlay is pleasingly small. For less than twenty-five dollars we can make a telescope that will satisfy every requirement for a good satellite-watching instrument.

Before we learn how to construct one, let us first decide what the requirements must be. We want a telescope with as wide a field as possible—for practical reasons, as we shall see, 12° is about as good as we can hope for. We want only a 5- or 6-power scope because low magnification means we can have other characteristics difficult to attain in high-powered instruments. Low powers are suitable for satellite watching. We want an exit pupil as large as the nighttime size of the pupil of the eye, and we need adequate eye relief for the sake of comfort. We would also like an instrument that we can use while sitting, but which will not limit us to this position.

Reviewing briefly some of the information given in chapter 3, we remember that:

Magnification = the focal length of the objective divided by the focal length of the eyepiece.

Field of view = the apparent field of the eyepiece divided by the magnification.

Exit pupil = the diameter of the objective divided by the magnification.

Eye relief = a distance which is always less than the focal length of the eyepiece.

Excellent design in a Moon-watch telescope. Notice that the eyepiece remains at a fixed height, a great advantage when changing the elevation, since the eye does not have to move. (Courtesy Smithsonian Astrophysical Observatory)

The best way to use these relationships in the construction of a Moon-watch telescope is to assume some arbitrary values and determine the characteristics of a hypothetical telescope from them. For this imaginary instrument we shall assume:

1. an objective lens whose diameter is 2 inches and whose focal length is 24 inches, and

2. two eyepieces that we may use interchangeably, each with an apparent field of 40° and focal lengths of ¼ inch and 2 inches respectively.

Using the relationships given above in terms of these specific characteristics, our hypothetical telescope will have the characteristics shown in the accompanying table.

	Telescope No. 1 (¼" eyepiece)	Telescope No. 2 (2" eyepiece)
Magnification	24 ÷ ¼ = 96	24 ÷ 2 = 12
Field of view	40 ÷ 96 = .41°	40 ÷ 12 = 3.33°
Exit pupil	2 ÷ 96 = 1/48"	2 ÷ 12 = 1/6"
Eye relief	less than ¼"	less than 2"

Neither eyepiece combination in this hypothetical telescope provides an instrument that will be of much use for satellite purposes, although No. 2 is considerably better than No. 1, based on the criteria for a good telescope. Yet it was worth making the table, for it yields considerable information. It shows, for example, that many of the characteristics of a telescope depend upon the focal length and apparent field of the eyepiece, and it also demonstrates that the focal length of the objective is of prime importance. Too long a focal length here will obviously produce too much magnification, no matter how long the focal length of the eyepiece.

Knowing these factors, we make another table, using an objective with a focal length of 7 inches (180 mm) and a diameter of 2 inches (51 mm). We choose this combination because it is produced by several lens manufacturers, is also available in war surplus stocks, and is therefore easy to obtain. Applying the lesson we just learned about eyepieces, we will choose two that have a large apparent field (in this case, 68°) and whose focal lengths are 1¼ inches and 2 inches respectively.

	Telescope No. 3 (1¼" eyepiece)	Telescope No. 4 (2" eyepiece)
Magnification	7 ÷ 1¼ = 5.6	7 ÷ 2 = 3.5
Field of view	68 ÷ 5.6 = 12.4°	68 ÷ 3.5 = 19.8°
Exit pupil	2 ÷ 5.6 = ⅜"	2 ÷ 3.5 = ⅝"
Eye relief	less than 1"	about 1½"

This combination gives two possibilities for satellite telescopes: telescope No. 3 matches almost exactly the characteristics we have already decided upon, but telescope No. 4 looks, at first glance, even better as far as field of view is concerned. Why not choose it then? In this case the wide field of view is accompanied by other characteristics that make the telescope as a whole undesirable. In our zeal to produce a super-field telescope we have also introduced distortions of the image. This is because of the nature of glass itself and there is nothing we can do about it. Telescope No. 3, however, makes an excellent satellite-watching scope. The optical parts are cheap and easy to obtain; the remaining parts are simple to construct from inexpensive materials.

The Moonwatch telescope, it must be added, is an astronomical instrument, which means that when used for looking around the countryside it produces an inverted image. This is an unhappy arrangement for watching a horse race, but it makes no difference to the astronomer, who cares little if the moon or a star is upside down in his telescope. We have not mentioned this characteristic before because, up until this point, we have been concerned with terrestrial instruments—for example, those used for looking around the countryside and which produce upright images. In order to change astronomical telescopes for terrestrial use we must add an extra lens to turn the image right side up. Binoculars have a prism system for this purpose; field glasses make use of a special type of eyepiece to accomplish it. Fortunately, in our Moonwatch telescope, an addition we make for another reason corrects part of this difficulty and we need not concern ourselves with extra lenses or prisms.

Since looking *up* at the sky is very tiresome, we adapt the telescope so we may look *down* and still see the sky. To do this we add a mirror at the front of the telescope which will reflect the image of the sky into the objective. We use what is called a first surface mirror for this purpose. Its front surface, instead of the back as in looking glasses, is silvered or aluminized. The addition of the mirror turns the image right side up but it is still reversed from right to left. In other words, a satellite passing across the sky from our right to our left will appear in the field of the telescope as going *from left to right*. Of course, the star field is *reversed* as well: the constellations appear as they would if we held a star chart against a bright light and looked at it from the back.

The mirror is attached to the telescope at a 45° angle. The result is that we see stars which are 90° away from the direction we are looking. The arrangement is comfortable physically, but confusing mentally until we get used to it. Fortunately a few practice sessions are enough to familiarize us with these quirks.

We can start by listing the materials we shall need (see appendix for purchasing details).

1. An achromatic objective of 180-mm focal length (about 7 inches) and 51-mm diameter (2 inches). This lens can be obtained in a mounted cell threaded on the outside and costs about $4.00.

2. An Erfle eyepiece of 1¼-inch focal length, 68° apparent field, and 2-inch outside diameter, costing about $15.00. Cheaper eyepieces may be obtained, but the large field of view of this one makes it well worth the price.

3. A first-surface mirror, 3 by 4 inches, costing $1.50. This combination of parts will produce an instrument of 5.5 power and over 12° field, an excellent satellite telescope. Although this is the recommended optical system, there are other combinations possible which will produce comparable performance. For example, the objective from a 7×50 binocular and any available wide-field eyepiece could be used. In any event, the expected performance should be carefully worked out on paper before any purchases are made, and these predictions should be verified on an optical bench after purchasing. A reputable dealer will make exchanges or permit returns when the performance of a particular item does not match the claims.

An optical bench is simply a device for lining up and testing optical parts. It is easily constructed from a yardstick and two wooden blocks made from 2 by 4's, grooved so they support the yardstick firmly. Two other blocks are similarly grooved and mounted to slide smoothly on top of the yardstick. These carry the optical parts and must be mounted so they do not interfere with the supporting blocks. Most optical benches have elaborate devices for holding lenses; but two lumps of modeling clay, one for each block, will permit any necessary adjustments of height or distance.

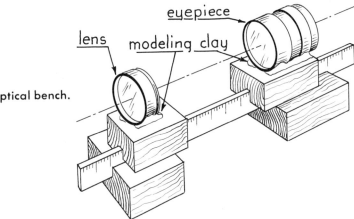

lens eyepiece modeling clay

Optical bench.

Slide the blocks together in the center of the yardstick until they touch. Mount the eyepiece on one and the objective on the other, adjusting the modeling clay until the centers of the two lenses are exactly aligned. Swing the whole arrangement around until the objective is pointing toward an *open* window, and train it on the most distant object that can be seen. Move the eyepiece block to the end of the yardstick away from the window, then move the objective toward the eyepiece until the distant object is in the sharpest possible focus. The image will, of course, be upside down; but do not worry since the purpose now is to achieve a sharp focus from a perfect alignment of the lenses. Once done, mark carefully the position of each lens on the yardstick. The two elements of the telescope are now properly spaced, exactly as they will be in the telescope tube.

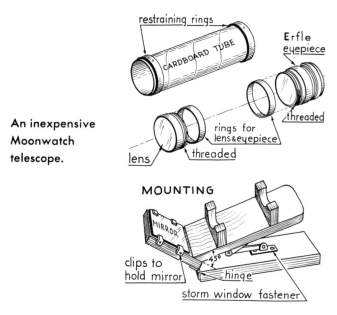

An inexpensive
Moonwatch
telescope.

Find a cardboard mailing tube with an inside diameter slightly larger than the outside diameter of the objective. Protect the glass surface of the lenses with circular pieces of tracing paper held in place with masking tape. Make a ring that fits tightly around the objective cell and fits snugly inside the tube. A simple way to do this is to cut strips of cardboard an inch wide and as long as possible. Wrap a strip of cardboard *tightly* around the metal ring in which the lens is mounted and glue (Carter's paper cement is best for this) the strip everywhere it overlaps. Build up strips until the ring fits very snugly inside the tube. Then make a similar ring for the eyepiece. After the glue has dried thoroughly, slip the rings off and put them aside until you have completed the next step.

Now cut the tube to the length determined by the measurements made on the optical bench. Be sure to square the ends exactly, since it is essential that the optical surfaces of objective and eyepiece be parallel to each other. Do this by wrapping a sheet of paper around the tube, lining up the edges of the paper carefully. Draw a line around the tube at the edge of the paper. Then, with a razor blade or sharp knife, cut along this line.

Glue the rings into each end of the tube, trimming off any projecting ends. Shellac the tube inside and out after the glue dries, then paint it with a *flat* black paint. Allow this to dry for at least twenty-four hours so that all the turpentine has surely evaporated.

After inserting the eyepiece and objective, test the telescope again on a distant object, preferably a star. If the star is round and sharp, the optical elements are properly positioned. But if the star appears to have a tail, the axes of the objective and eyepiece are not lined up properly and must be adjusted until the star test indicates satisfactory alignment. Mark this final position of the optical elements carefully for this will be their permanent position in the tube.

The cells of the optical parts—that is, the casings in which they are mounted when you buy them—are usually threaded on the outside. If a drop or two of airplane cement is placed on the threads and the cells are screwed into the tube, a firm bond will be established and the optical parts will be in no danger of falling or slipping out of the tube. But the use of airplane cement near optical surfaces is likely to have bad consequences unless great care is taken to avoid smearing any cement on the glass. If this happens in spite of your care, you can remove the cement by using a few drops of acetone or ethyl acetate on a soft cloth. Rub the glass surface gently until the cement is absorbed.

To make even more certain that the optical parts are permanently fixed in the tube, make a pair of inch-wide restraining rings to fit on the outside of the tube. These can be made from the thin, metal tubing found around almost any plumbing establishment or supply house. Drill and tap the restraining rings for set screws, then turn the screws up until they bear firmly against the cells of the optical parts. These restraining rings are not strictly necessary, since cementing the optical elements into position is usually enough. In any case, if the work has been done carefully, the result is a lighttight and airtight telescope.

Some people will not trust good optical elements to a cardboard tube. Since aluminum tubing is inexpensive and strong, it makes a good substitute for cardboard. Moreover, it can be threaded to fit the threads of the optical elements. Unless the cells of the eyepiece and the objective, however, are exactly the same size, other tubing or rings must be added to make the parts fit.

One such arrangement is shown in the photograph. Here the objective was obtained by unscrewing the whole front element from a pair of Japanese 7×50 binoculars. The photograph shows how diameters of the objective and the eyepiece vary considerably. The problem was solved by using two aluminum caps of the right size forced over the ends of the aluminum tubing. The caps were threaded to fit the objective and the eyepiece. The result is a sturdy telescope capable of withstanding much rough treatment.

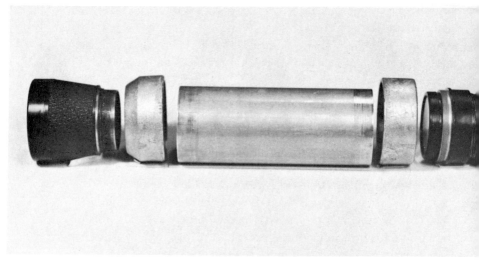

A Moonwatch telescope expanded to show details of construction. The objective is the front end of a 7×50 pair of binoculars. (Millbrook School Photo Service)

MOUNTING A MOONWATCH TELESCOPE

The telescope can be mounted in a variety of ways. This is not a precise job; for, once the mounting is in position, it requires no fine adjustments. Any mounting, therefore, that holds the telescope firmly and without vibration is adequate.

A very simple mount can be made from ¾-inch plywood, a ¾-by-2-inch hinge, a storm-window fastener with 4-inch arms, some metal clips made from ¼-inch brass angles with ¾-inch arms, and some heavy elastic bands.

Cut out two curved supports for the telescope tube, using a band saw or coping saw. Then cut out two pieces of plywood, one 5 by 3¼ inches and the other 9 by 3¼ inches. Make a 45° cut at the end of the 9-inch piece, using a miter box to make sure it is exactly 45°. Screw the two pieces of wood together so the surface of the small piece fits on the 45° angle of the

onger piece. Check carefully with a protractor to be sure that the angle the
two pieces make with each other is exactly 135°. Now mount the two
curved pieces of wood on this combination. Clean up the curves with a
wood rasp until they fit the tube snugly.

A simplified version of the Moonwatch telescope. (Millbrook School
Photo Service)

Cut another piece of plywood, this time 10 by 7¼ inches. Attach this
piece to the other two as shown in the diagram, using the hinge for this
purpose. Make sure there is complete freedom of motion between the two
sections and that this motion is at right angles. Check this by holding a
square on the baseboard and moving the jointed section up and down. If
the top section follows the arm of the square the two pieces are at right
angles.

55

Apply the storm-window fastener as shown, making sure it permit free motion yet is stiff enough so the two sections will remain in any relative position in which they are placed. A nut at the base of the storm window fastener adjusts it to any degree of flexibility.

Clips for the mirror are easily made from small brass right angles Mount them on the sides of the mirror support, glue pieces of felt on their inside surfaces to prevent scarring the mirror, and bend them over until they hold the mirror securely in place. Be sure the mirror is located so it center point is directly in line with the optical axis of the telescope.

Place the telescope on its supports and secure it with one or two heavy elastic bands. Make sure that the bands have enough tension to hold the telescope in its cradle without slipping, but place them close together so they can be removed quickly and easily.

Place this assembly on a low table or tripod. The tripod is preferable since its height can be adjusted to the most comfortable position for the observer. But whatever basic support is used, table or tripod, it must be absolutely level. Test the action of the instrument by focusing it on the top of a flagpole or the corner of a high building. When the telescope is depressed it should follow the flagpole all the way to the ground without further alignment. If it does not, the trouble will lie in any of three possibilities: (1) the tripod may not be level, (2) the mirror may be tipped a little to the right or left on its base, or (3) the hinge may have been placed so the action of the two parts of the mount are not at right angles. Check the first two possibilities thoroughly before investigating the third.

USING THE TELESCOPE

Once the telescope and mount are functioning properly, we are ready to put the instrument to use. Using a satellite finder, determine the direction and angle in the sky where the satellite will appear at the high point of its arc. Subtract this angle from 90°, and cut a piece of cardboard to the resulting angle. Adjust the base of the telescope to it. To use a practical example, if the satellite is expected to cross the meridian at an angle of 38°, then 90° − 38° = 52°, and this is the angle at which the instrument must be set. The reason for this is understood if we remember that when the base of the telescope is vertical, the mirror will give a direct view of the horizon If the mirror is tipped up 38°, the base of the telescope must be tipped down 38°, which still leaves an angle of 52° between the base and the top of the table or tripod.

If the satellite is to cross the sky from northwest to southeast in the western sky, point the telescope southwest so the satellite will cross the ield at right angles. Remember again that, because of the way satellite telescopes are constructed, if the satellite is crossing the sky from right to left, it will appear to cross the field of the telescope from left to right. Therefore we direct our attention to the left side of the field. Depending on the height at which the satellite is flying, it will take from 10 to 15 seconds to cross the field of the telescope. As it crosses the field to the right side, turn the telescope on its base to follow it, at the same time adjusting the angle to compensate for changes in altitude. This sounds easier than it is in practice, so an alternative procedure is to snap off the elastic bands, pick the telescope up, and follow the satellite with the telescope held in the hands. Since the interval between sighting a satellite and its final disappearance is usually several minutes, there is plenty of time to do this. But try it on an airplane several times before your first satellite-watching jaunt.

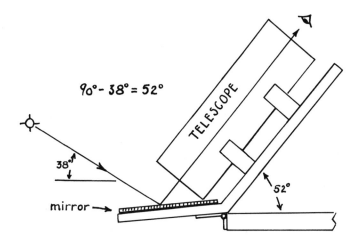

Subtract the expected altitude of the satellite from 90° and set the telescope to the result.

Chapter 5

The Moonwatch Program

Moonwatch is the name of the world-wide project for which interested amateurs observe and report passages of satellites. The name, of course, refers to artificial "moons." The program is part of the huge organization set up to coordinate and report scientific findings during the International Geophysical Year. Its specific function is to determine the position of any satellite within a degree of arc and the second of time when it occupied that position.

The Moonwatch program is the particular responsibility of the Smithsonian Astrophysical Observatory, under the direction of Drs. Fred L. Whipple and J. A. Hynek. The teams which report their observations to the headquarters at Cambridge, Massachusetts, are organized by Mr. Leon Campbell, Jr. These men have set up an organization whose streamlined operations must be the envy of efficiency experts. Even though the Moonwatch teams were not developed to full capacity when the scientific world was caught unprepared by the launching of the first Russian Sputnik, they went into action as though they had been expecting the event. Headquarters handled 391 reports from 135 different teams during the short life of the satellite. Accurate, day-by-day predictions were made of the satellite's position throughout its life.

The project represents what is possibly the greatest concerted effort ever made by layman to help a scientific program. Its membership cuts through national and racial lines and includes groups from at least fifteen countries. The teams are scattered all over the world, with the greatest concentration in the United States and Japan. There are groups in Ar-

entina, Australia, the Belgian Congo, Canada, Chile, Ecuador, Mexico, the
Netherlands Antilles, Peru, Uruguay, and the Union of South Africa. The
system mushroomed from the establishment of the first station in Silver
Spring, Maryland, in late 1956, until at the launching of the first Explorer there were 220 teams on the alert. Since then, on an average, two
teams a week have been added to the roster. This list does not include inde-
pendent observers or the hundreds of teams in Russia, nor does it take in
the many members of photographic units or radio-tracking organizations.
All told, there are at least three thousand people in an official status watching some stage of the satellite's passage.

Distribution of Moonwatch teams.

Every Moonwatch team is composed of from twenty to one hundred
members. There is a leader in charge, aided by a deputy; the remaining
members serve as observers, data recorders, radio operators, tape-recorder
operators, messengers, and electricians. It is best to have plenty of people on
hand, though only sixteen telescopes are needed, because fatigue makes a
systematic relief imperative. The observing periods are often long and
tedious, conditions for observing are sometimes very unfavorable (one
team actually carried out a before-dawn alert when the temperature was
16° below zero), and such circumstances make frequent changes of observers necessary.

Many volunteers for Moonwatch teams have had some astronomical
experience, perhaps as amateurs in local astronomy clubs, or have learned
something about the heavens as a result of building their own telescopes.
But some start their association with a team knowing little more about
astronomy than the location of the Big Dipper. The common, and most important, factor is enthusiasm. There is a team composed only of parents,

who take their children with them, another which consists of the members of a college faculty, and a third whose members are schoolboys from a preparatory school. But these are exceptions, since the members of most groups come from all walks of life; schoolteachers and their pupils, bankers, policemen, auto mechanics, housewives, all working for a common purpose. The teams receive support from many sources. There are, for example, teams from the armed services (acting in a nonmilitary status, but using equipment supplied by their units) and teams supported by newspapers, astronomical societies, banks, industrial concerns, colleges, and universities.

Each team must supply its own equipment—a considerable expense in most cases, since the minimum equipment for a group costs about two thousand dollars. Working hours (often bleak and chilly periods before dawn and after dusk) are those no sensible human would choose for a volunteer effort. The members of these teams receive no pay or recognition. They are satisfied by the knowledge that they are taking part in an exploration that will one day benefit mankind.

Most teams require, for new members, a short course in basic astronomy. Older members are usually the teachers. The students learn about key constellations, about the apparent motion of the stars, how to use star charts, how time varies throughout the world, how stars are located by using chart coordinates, and the meanings of astronomical terms. Then they study the general characteristics of satellites and their orbits. After this basic indoctrination, each member learns how to use his telescope (first, in the case of many teams, how to build it!). The discipline and techniques of team observations must be stressed by the teachers so that the duties of each observer can be coordinated with those of the rest of the group. The individual member, for example, must narrow the scope of his observing and assume responsibility only for the particular area of the sky to which he is assigned. He is not allowed to move his telescope to follow a satellite under any circumstance, since this may break the continuity of the team's observations.

A Moonwatch station is set up to provide an optical fence along the meridian of its particular location. To explain how this works, let us suppose that we could build a real fence of infinite height so it passed through our observing site from north to south. The top of the fence would cut an arc in the heavens which we call the meridian of our location. Any object passing through the sky at right angles to this arc would have to pass through it at some point along its length. Since we cannot construct such a fence, we do the next best thing and set up a series of telescopes which are located in such a way that they keep every point in the meridian under observation. This arrangement is called an optical fence, and any satellite passing through it must be observed in one of the telescopes.

Model of Moonwatch station. At the base of the mast is the timing equipment. Notice the parallel between this model and the actual set-up shown in the frontispiece. (Courtesy Smithsonian Astrophysical Observatory)

There are several ways in which the optical fence may be set up. In one of them a mast, some thirty feet high, is erected in a level area, and the telescopes are distributed along a north-south line running through its foot. The field of view of each telescope is centered on the top of the mast at the junction of a crossbar also mounted in a north-south line. The crossbar serves as a lateral extension of the mast for observers located close to its base. Since each telescope is trained on the same point on the mast, those nearest its base will cover higher elevations in the sky and ones farther away will provide coverage for elevations closer to the horizon. As we learned earlier, Moonwatch telescopes cover a field of 12°. The meridian is divided into 10° sections, so there will be an overlap in the fields of any two adjacent telescopes. The spacing of the telescopes thus becomes a problem in trigonometry, where the height of the mast and the angle of each instrument makes with its top is known. Using a table of tangents, we can determine the distance of each telescope from its foot.

This sounds more complicated than it actually turns out to be. Suppose, for example, we wish to cover one of the segments of the meridian extending between altitudes of 75° and 85°. We do this by placing the telescope at the right distance from the foot of the mast so that when it is trained on the top its line of view will be inclined to an angle of 80°. Thus it will cover the middle and both ends of the segment. But we must find the distance first.

Let us say the mast is 33 feet high and the telescope will be placed on a 3-foot table. The vertical distance from the telescope to the top of the mast, then, must be 30 feet. If we refer to the diagram we see that the two distances, the height of the mast and the distance of the table from it, are the legs of a right triangle. In trigonometry the relationship of these two legs is called the tangent, and the formula we use is

$$\text{tangent } 80° = \frac{\text{height of the mast (30 feet)}}{\text{distance from the base}}.$$

We find, from a table of trigonometric functions (see appendix), that the tangent of $80° = 5.67$. Substituting this in the equation we have,

$$5.67 = \frac{30}{\text{distance from the base}} \quad \text{or,}$$

$$\text{distance from the base} = \frac{30}{5.67} = 5 \text{ feet } 3 \text{ inches.}$$

Thus, if we place the table at this distance with the telescope pointed at the top of the mast, we are assured of covering the section of the meridian between 75° and 85°. Using this method, we proceed to place the rest of the telescopes so they will cover the whole meridian in 10° segments. A difficulty awaits us here, however, for when we come to place the final two telescopes (those that will be pointed toward sections of the sky near the horizon), we find we must place them so far from the mast they will be a long way from the rest of the observers. A little thought will show us that we can take care of this situation simply by training these instruments on a lower point on the mast.

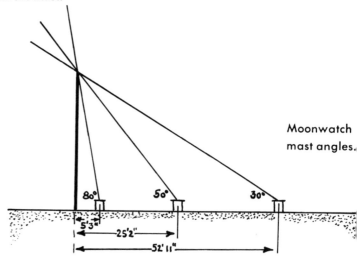

Moonwatch
mast angles.

An artificial meridian placed in front of the field lens of the eyepiece. Some Moonwatch teams prefer this arrangement to the mast shown in other photographs. (Millbrook School Photo Service)

Another method eliminates the mast and replaces it with an artificial meridian within the telescope itself. A wire, mounted just inside the field lens of the eyepiece (see photograph), serves this purpose. The advantage is that the telescopes may be placed parallel to each other at a table instead of in a line. Each observer can then easily hear what is happening and he is near the recording instruments. The disadvantage is that a north-south line must be established for each telescope and that some means must be provided to set each one at its proper altitude. Furthermore, a way must be found to insure that each of the artificial meridians is truly vertical.

A third method depends upon neither a meridian mast nor an artificial meridian within the telescope, but upon the star background in the field of view and the ability of the observer to reconstruct the passage of the satellite across the same field as it appears on in a star chart. The position of the satellite now can be read directly from the chart, or determined by the azimuth and altitude of the telescope itself. This method is especially useful in the case of Russian satellites which cross the sky along a north-south instead of east-west line. These intersect the meridian at such a shallow angle that it is difficult to place them exactly. The principle of the optical fence is not lost here, for the telescopes are still placed so they cover the sky from horizon to zenith. All telescopes are oriented on the mast as before, in order to set them for the proper elevation, then each is swiveled exactly 45° on its base to left or right depending on which side the satellite will pass.

Timing the instant of passage is done by means of a short-wave radio and a tape recorder. The radio is tuned to the time signals of the National Bureau of Standards in Washington, D.C. (station WWV), the Dominion Observatory in Canada (Station CBU), or any other available source. The signals are given at intervals of one second, with the announcer breaking in periodically to give the base time in minutes (see appendix for full details of transmissions). The tape recorder picks up and continuously records the time signals.

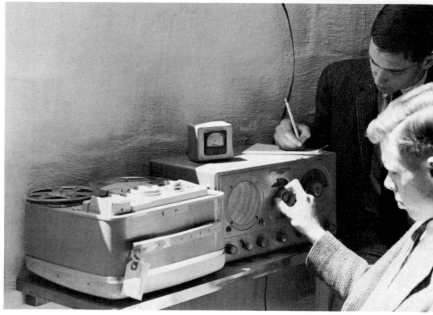

Tape recorder and short-wave radio used for timing passages of satellites. (Millbrook School Photo Service)

When an observer sees a satellite enter the field of his telescope, he either presses a buzzer or shouts "Mark." He repeats the same call at the moment the satellite crosses the meridian line, and again when it leaves his field. These calls are recorded on the same tape which is "taking down" the time ticks—the calls are superimposed on the time signals. When the tape is played back it gives the exact moment that the satellite first entered the field of the telescope, then crossed the meridian, and finally passed out of the field. In other words, it gives the *total time* for the satellite to pass clear across the field of the telescope. From this one calculates its speed in degrees per second. Suppose, for example, our observer has an interval of ten seconds between his first and last call. If the satellite passed exactly across the center of his 12° field, its speed must have been 1.2° per second.

But the observer saw the satellite in the *sky*. If computation centers are to use his observation to plot an orbit for the satellite, they must know what its position would be on a *chart*. There are two ways this information can be obtained. First, the observer can report his exact geographical location in latitude and longitude, the altitude of the satellite as seen through his telescope, and the azimuth (direction in which the telescope was pointed). Each of these figures must be reported to the nearest degree. This information, plus the time the satellite was seen, is enough for the great IBM computers to convert into an exact satellite position. An alternative method is for the observer himself to work out the position. To do this, he notes the meridian line as it was seen against the background of stars at the moment of observation, then transfers the meridian to its corresponding position relative to the same stars on a chart. He marks the point where the satellite crossed the meridian and finds the coordinates of this point from the scales of right ascension and declination at the sides of the chart, as shown on the diagram. Moonwatch teams use the *Skalnate Pleso* charts for plotting purposes. (See appendix as to where these excellent charts may be obtained.)

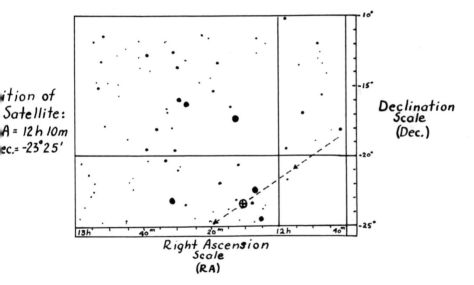

Plotting a satellite's position.

A third method is to dispense with the meridian line altogether and use the star background in the telescope's field. Here the observer estimates how close the satellite passes to a bright star, or a configuration of stars, and plots this position on the chart, reading the coordinates in the same way as before.

The result of any of these methods is an exact satellite position for a particular moment of time. This is telegraphed to the Smithsonian Astrophysical Observatory where it is combined with similar reports from other Moonwatch teams. All reports are fed into an IBM 704 computer which can determine an orbit based on them within a few minutes. It is thus possible to acquire exact information about a satellite within an hour after its passage and to base predictions about subsequent passages on this information.

Two views of the IBM 704 Data Processing System. These giant computers are used to predict satellite passages based on observations already made. (Courtesy International Business Machines Corporation)

A Moonwatch report usually includes more information than the position and time of the passage of a satellite. A complete report has the following items (see glossary for definitions of technical terms):

1. Descriptive information about the station from which the report originates. This is given by the team designation, a group of nine digits showing the team number and the latitude and longitude of the station. For example, the designation of the team at Millbrook, New York, is 045 042 074, which means team number 45, located at latitude 42° north and 74° west.

2. Date of the observation in Universal Time.

3. Time of the observation in Universal Time (to the nearest second).

4. The right ascension, or azimuth (to the nearest minute).

5. Declination, or altitude (to the nearest minute).

6. Direction of travel.

7. Magnitude.

8. Angular velocity (in degrees per second).

9. Color.

Although information about a satellite is valuable at any time during its life, there are three periods when it is most important:

1. *The Acquisition Period.* As soon as a satellite is launched and in orbit, the job of finding it begins. If its radio is functioning, its signals can be picked up by the Minitrack stations, a line of specially constructed receivers located along a north-south axis in the Western Hemisphere. This is a radio fence comparable to the optical fence of the Moonwatch system. The Minitrack cannot give an exact position. The surest method of determining a provisional orbit is by visual sightings. During the period immediately after a launching, therefore, all Moonwatch teams are expected to maintain a complete alert, with all available instruments in use. To be really effective, an alert at this time must extend through the complete twilight periods before dawn and after dusk, an interval of two hours each. After enough sightings have been made to establish a preliminary orbit, the teams modify their operating procedures, and the next period begins.

2. *The Tracking Period.* This stage, depending on the characteristics of the orbit, will last some time. Teams are expected to observe whenever the satellite may be visible over their stations. By now enough information will have been gathered so that the area of observations can be limited to a relatively small arc of the sky. Since this requires fewer telescopes, the whole team is not alerted; subgroups take turns observing.

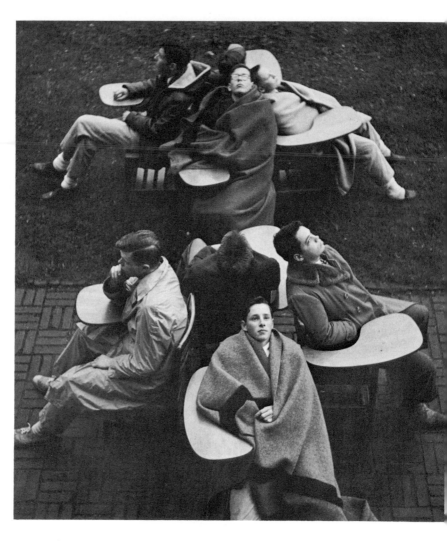

Looking for the "dying moments" of a satellite. The time of appearance and exact direction are not certain during this period. The watchers are therefore covering all points of the horizon. No telescopes are needed since the satellite is very bright. (Millbrook School Photo Service)

The tracking period was not originally intended to be a Moonwatch function, since it was expected that, by the time the satellites actually appeared in the sky, the great Baker-Nunn tracking cameras would have been completed and in operation. These cameras are so accurate that they can pinpoint the position of a satellite to a degree impossible with ordinary telescopic sightings. For the early satellites, however, the cameras were not ready for action, and the tracking was done by Moonwatch groups.

3. *The "Dying Moments" Period.* A falling satellite produces a great deal of information about the density of the atmosphere through which it plunges. Again Moonwatch teams everywhere are put on full alert. The satellite's path, within limits, and expected time of fall are known. But the observing technique is different at this time, for telescopes are put aside in favor of naked-eye observation. The friction of the atmosphere heats the satellite until it glows from its own light. For this reason it can be seen throughout the night, and watches are maintained from dusk until dawn instead of during the usual observing periods. The teams are divided into subgroups, each taking a two-hour watch period, and the vigil is maintained until it is definitely known that the satellite has fallen. The teams, at this time, are looking for definite characteristics such as speed, direction, magnitude, and color.

Part of the Millbrook Moonwatch team. The observatory in the background was built by the boys as part of a science project. (Millbrook School Photo Service)

In its final moments, a dying satellite is indeed a spectacular sight, one never to be forgotten. The two Moonwatch teams (Millbrook, New York, and Bryn Athyn, Pennsylvania) who saw Sputnik II in its final passage over the east coast of the United States, said that it had a tail like a comet and that it seemed to pulsate as it raced across the sky just before its final plunge into the waters of the Caribbean Sea, ten minutes later.

Thus the Moonwatch teams follow satellites practically from birth to destruction. The contributions they have made to the whole satellite program have been, and will continue to be, invaluable. Leon Campbell, the supervisor of Moonwatch Station Operations, has written:

"It is significant that the 'Moonwatch' Operation undoubtedly has constituted the greatest continuous participation on the part of the public in an astronomical program. It is difficult to assess the intangible benefits to the public's scientific awareness that the 'Moonwatch' Operation has engendered."

Chapter 6

Photographing the Satellites

The action of the photographer in taking a picture of a satellite is almost a passive one. He doesn't attempt to "stop" the satellite to get its picture at a single point in the orbit. Instead, he concentrates on taking a time exposure of a good, clear star field and hopes the satellite will photograph itself by forming a light trace across the emulsion of his film as it passes through the star field.

PHOTOGRAPHY FOR FUN

Photographing of satellites is practically a new field in photography; very little has been done in it and there are no hard and fast rules. Consequently, taking a good photograph of a satellite is as challenging a problem as the amateur (or professional) photographer can find. He must get a nighttime photograph of a moving object whose brightness, point of appearance, and direction of travel he is only reasonably sure of. He must work under the rapidly changing lighting characteristic of dawn and dusk. He cannot be certain of his exposure time or camera opening since he can't use an exposure meter. A well-known authority on photography, Aaron Sussman,[1] says that under conditions such as these one must simply try out a dozen shots to get the hang of it. But this is just what the satellite photographer can't do; if he misses his first shot he doesn't get another chance. Perhaps it is this challenge that makes photographing the satellites so much fun.

[1] *The Amateur Photographer's Handbook,* Thomas Y. Crowell Company, New York, 1958.

*Millbrook School
Photo Service*

We have overstated the case a little, for in spite of these difficultie many good pictures of satellites have been taken. Patience, a few carefu preparations, and a certain amount of luck will sooner or later result in a picture we can be proud of.

Our first consideration is the camera. Almost any camera of f/4.5 o better will do. The normal field of view for a camera lens is about 50°; thi is plenty wide enough for satellite photography. If we want to be a little more certain that we will catch the elusive "moon," we can buy a wide-angle lens which will cover a quarter of the sky. Depending on the camera used there are wide-angle lenses available for fields of view up to 140° or more The Zeiss Hypergon (140° field; speed f/22) and the Meyer Aristostigma (105° field; f/6.3 speed) are good examples. However, increasing the field will decrease the size of the image, as we found in the chapter on binoculars If we are careful in orienting the camera, there is really no need for such wide fields.

This brings up the question of exposure time. A satellite travels with an angular velocity which varies with its position in the orbit—figures on Sputnik I ranged from 0.2° to 2.5° per second. If we accept the middle value of these estimates, say 1°, a satellite would take 50 seconds to cross a 50° field of view. Hence the longest exposure we need is about 50 seconds if we want the longest possible satellite trace on the film.

But long exposures bring in other problems. If the sky is illuminated—ay just before dawn or if there is a bright moon—a long exposure will result n an overexposed negative. On the other hand, if we cut down the exposure ime we shorten the satellite trace on the film. Judging the time of exposure nder these conditions so that we will get the longest possible satellite trace s largely a matter of practice based on using up some film for experimental urposes. Load the camera, set up the tripod, and take some star pictures nder varying light conditions of twilight, using a range of exposure times. A roll or two of film and a few hours of time will produce enough experience o cope with the light conditions encountered when the satellite goes by. In the meantime, you may acquire some good star pictures.)

The question of satellite brightness is an important one here. If, in your ractice sessions, you work out exposure times and camera openings that vill bring in only bright stars, a dim satellite will leave no trace at all on the ilm. So you must set the camera to bring in faint stars; if the satellite trace s, as a consequence, a little overexposed, you will at least have a picture of it. Moreover, the satellite is moving and will not build up on the emulsion an image as strong as those of the motionless stars which are pouring light on one spot throughout the exposure.

Photo of 1957 alpha (Sputnik I) taken by Raymond Grenchik of Louisiana State University. Made with a 4-inch, f/5 camera, exposure time 3 seconds. Mr. Grenchik says that the interrupted trail at the beginning of the exposure was caused by vibration as the dust cap was removed. (Courtesy Raymond Grenchik)

Most of the good satellite photographs produced to date have bee made with a lens opening of around f/4. But experience is again the be teacher here and you may find that your finest star pictures come fro values above or below this one. If so, it is the best for satellites.

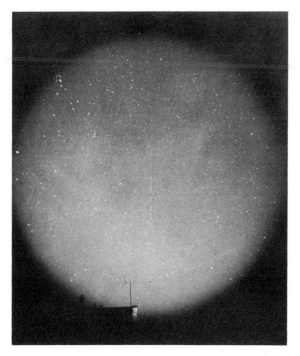

Another photograph Sputnik I taken by Joh F. Gregory of Sprin dale, Connecticut. This a chopped-trail phot graph taken with a Pe kin-Elmer 3-inch, f/1 lens on Royal X Pa Each exposure is a proximately 3 second with 3-second interva between. (Courtesy Joh F. Gregory)

Next, the film used. High-speed emulsions are best. If you have 35-mm camera, try DuPont SX Pan, Ilford HP3 or HPS, Kodak Tri-X, any other film having the characteristics of those named. They all have a ASA exposure index of from 200 to 600. For larger cameras, using roll filr or film packs, Ilford HP3 and Kodak Tri-X are good possibilities. In shee film, the range is wider: Royal X Pan, Royal Pan, Royal Ortho, DuPont H Speed Pan type 428, or Ansco Triple-S Pan. This is quite a long list, nc intended to imply that you should experiment with all of them to find th best one for satellite photography. Quite the contrary is true. Work wit only one kind until you know how it behaves under a variety of condition. The same is true for developing, except to a lesser degree. The best de veloper is usually the one recommended by the manufacturer of the film You may want to experiment a little here, though, since you are workin with a type of photograph the manufacturer didn't anticipate. For exampl Royal X Pan of ASA rating 800 may be developed using DK-60A, DK-5(or Extol UFG. But once you find a film and developer combination that yo like, stay with it.

Having completed enough experiments so you are satisfied your camera
ill take a picture of the satellite, once it appears, turn to other preparations
 a more immediate nature. The first of these is to make sure that your
amera is firmly supported. Because the least vibration will make the
atellite trace look like a photograph of a sound wave, use a sturdy, de-
endable tripod. Or another arrangement that works well is to mount the
amera on the tube of a heavy, vibration-free telescope. Line up the fields
f view of the camera and telescope so they are centered on the same area.
his will help later in setting the camera to the proper elevation.

Make sure that you have an accurate prediction for the passage of the
atellite: its time, where it will appear in the sky, its altitude, and the direc-
on of the sub-satellite point. The best photographs can be obtained when
ae satellite is at its maximum altitude, since the density of the atmosphere
ecreases with increased height. Of the several sources predicting the ap-
earance of satellites discussed in chapter 2, the best for photography is the
precast provided by the Civil Air Patrol network each weekday night.
hese forecasts are especially valuable in that they include twilight and
clipse information based on the most up-to-date predictions available.

Now let us assume that the highest altitude predicted for a satellite
n a given passage is 50°. A sighting device to find this altitude in the sky
aay be made easily by sighting along the side of a protractor, using a pencil
s a line of sight. Point the base of the protractor in the direction of the
xpected sub-satellite point, keeping the protractor level by holding its
ase on the corner of a table. Swing the pencil up to the 50° mark on the
rotractor, and it will now point to within a degree or two of the satellite's
xpected altitude. Pick out a star in this area, then set the camera at an angle
hat will bring the star into the center of the field of the view finder.

A few minutes before the satellite is expected, set the lens opening for
he conditions prevailing at the time (this is where your previous experience
ith star photography will pay dividends), place a piece of cardboard in
ront of the lens, and open the shutter. The cardboard is a precaution
gainst vibration; unless you have a very long cable release its action may
ar the camera enough to produce a wavy satellite trace on the film. If the
ind is blowing, place your body to protect the camera from its force. On
he other hand, if there is no breeze and the temperature is changing, watch
ut for dewing conditions. The camera lens may be soaked before you re-
lize it, and you will have no time to clean it when the satellite is overhead.

When the satellite appears, remove the cardboard to start the exposure.
f you have a source of time signals, such as WWV, break the exposure
very second or two by holding the cardboard in front of the lens; and make
 record of the exact time the exposure is over. Also make a note of the
onstellations through which the satellite passes and identify the principal

stars in the field. The exact conditions under which the photograph was taken—such as the clarity of the sky and the amount of light, the temperature, and the location and phase of the moon—are worthy of record since they are all informative data which will make your next picture better.

A telescope may be used as a camera by equipping it with a plate holder placed either at the prime focus or at the eyepiece. This use is discouraged, however, since an inherent difficulty is the small field. A refracting telescope of 84-inch focal length covers only 1/14 of the field of view of a camera whose focal length is 6 inches. And if the eyepiece of the telescope is used to project an image on the plate, the field is even smaller. In other words, using a telescope as a camera narrows the field until it is almost useless as a means of photographing satellites. We mention it here only because some readers may wonder why telescopes are not ordinarily used this way.

The telescope shown in the foreground is excellent for ordinary astronomical purposes but useless for observing and photographing satellites because of the small field of view. (Millbrook School Photo Service)

Added to the two chief fields of amateur satellite observation—Moon-
atch, or visual watching, and Moonbeam,[2] or radio observation—is a third
fficial program. Known as Program Phototrack, this organization was
ormed early in 1958 to supplement the work of the great Baker-Nunn
acking cameras. It is formally endorsed by the USNC-IGY[3] and is actively
upported by the Society of Photographic Scientists and Engineers. The
specifications for the conditions under which the photographs are taken, as
vell as for the photographs themselves, are very rigid; but this will not keep
many amateur photographers from attempting to live up to them and from
articipating in the program.

Phototrack requires negatives of at least 4 by 5 inches, produced by a
ens of at least 5-inch focal length. They must show the trace of the satellite
rbit (not the satellite itself) against a fixed background of stars. The trace
must contain at least two gaps, or displacements, timed to an accuracy of
tenth of a second. The required accuracy in timing will do more to dis-
ourage amateurs than any other single factor, for it requires timing devices
ot ordinarily available. But accurate timing is absolutely necessary for
Phototrack purposes.

The accuracy of an astronomical photograph is astonishing to most
f us. If it shows a satellite path of appreciable length among the stars, say
5° or 20°, it represents the satellite's path within 50 yards. Such accuracy
n a photograph requires that all positions on the trace be equally accurate,
nd this calls for extremely precise timing devices.

If the observing station is near a source of 60-cycle power, an auxiliary
amera equipped with an electronic flash unit can photograph the time on
large synchronous clock. The date and location of the station must be
osted near the clock so the photograph will contain all necessary data
nd thus need no supplementary information. The auxiliary camera is set
up indoors, if possible, and is wired to the Phototrack camera itself in such
way that, when the satellite passes, two photographs will be taken simul-
aneously: one of the satellite and one of the exact time. This is done, as
hown in the illustration, by connecting a metal part of the Phototrack
amera tripod and a metal striking tool to the flash circuit. This tool, which
must be heavy enough to jar the camera slightly, closes the flash circuit
when it is struck against the tripod. A third piece of equipment is a short-
wave radio capable of picking up WWV time signals.

[2] The address of the Moonbeam program is National Academy of Sciences, IGY
Earth Satellite Office, 2101 Constitution Avenue, Washington 25, D.C.
[3] United States National Committee for the International Geophysical Year.

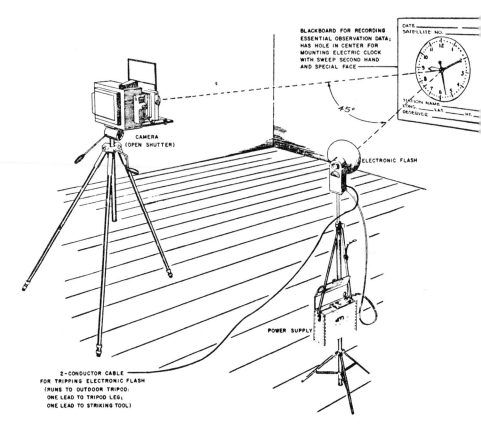

Above: auxiliary camera set up to photograph precise times of breaks in satellite's track shown on Phototrack negatives. *Below:* representation of Phototrack print showing path of 1957 beta (Sputnik II). Break in track shows point at which camera was rapped. (From *IGY Bulletin;* used by permission of USNC-IGY)

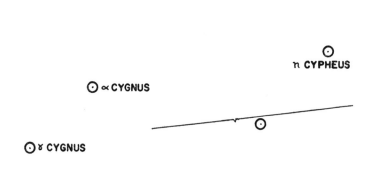

Shortly before the expected approach of the satellite, the clock is set correspond exactly to the time ticks received on the radio. Then all lights e turned off and the shutters of both cameras are opened.

As the satellite passes overhead and its image approaches the center the field of the Phototrack camera, the circuit is closed by tapping the ipod with the metal connector, thus setting off the flash unit and photographing the time with the auxiliary camera. This is done again within a few conds to obtain a second photograph of the time. Both of these photographs of the time are recorded on the same film, the result being merely show the second hand of the clock in two different positions. Finally, to rve as a check on the synchronous clock, the circuit is once more closed ter the exposure is complete, this time on the fifth second after the double ck on WWV. This double tick appears at the beginning of each minute ee appendix) in the WWV time transmissions. If the clock inside, when e third picture is taken of its face, shows its second hand on the 5-second ark, it is, of course, evident that all times on the clock are correct. The ader may find it hard to believe that the observer can manually hit the ipod at exactly the fifth second. If so, he has only to remember that times corded in track meets, using manual timing, are recorded to a tenth of a cond.

The final result of the procedure is two photographs, one showing a tellite trace with two jogs resulting from the tremors induced when the g of the tripod was struck, and the other showing two times which exactly orrespond to the jogs. The third time serves merely as a check on the whole rocedure. In other words, the photographs now constitute a complete timed cord of a satellite passage in which the data is self-evident.

But if this highly instrumented setup is not possible, a reasonably close pproach to the desired accuracy may be made using only the WWV time ignals. While one member of the group keeps track of time by counting me ticks—or better still, making a written record of it—another drops a ardboard slide before the lens simultaneously with a tick and holds it there or several seconds. The result is an interruption in the filmed path of the atellite the duration of which is known at least to the nearest second. The ccuracy can be increased somewhat by using a stop watch in conjunction ith the beginning and end of the timed period when the lens is covered. he camera shutter should not be used to produce the break in the satellite race since few cameras have shutters whose action is consistent. Those who ave tried photography on a very cold day, for example, have found this ut to their sorrow.

But if the difficulties mentioned above are not enough to discourage mateur photographers, the Phototrack program has another complication. his is the problem of station location. In determining the exact position of a passing heavenly body, satellite or otherwise, it is necessary to know the precise location of the observer. While Moonwatch stations need give their positions only to the nearest minute of latitude and longitude, for camera tracking purposes this is not close enough. A requirement of the Phototrack program is that the camera must be located at a U.S. Coast and Geodetic Survey Triangulation Marker. This does not mean precisely on top of one of these markers, of course, but within very accurate measuring distance of one. The requirement turns out to be more of an annoyance than a serious complication since there are over 100,000 of these markers in the United States. Their location is shown as dots within circles on the topographic maps which can be obtained from the U.S. Geological Survey in Washington, D.C., or from local surveyors' offices.

Film and camera requirements vary with the brightness of the satellite. The Russian satellites can be photographed at f/4.5 with films having an ASA exposure index of 200, developed in D-19 for 5.5 minutes at 68° F. On the other hand, a satellite leaving a fainter trace, such as the larger Vanguards, requires an opening of 2.8 or better and superfast emulsions having exposure indexes in the vicinity of ASA 1,600. By using such fast emulsions, along with forced development techniques and lenses of 4-inch aperture, it is possible to photograph almost any satellite now in the skies.

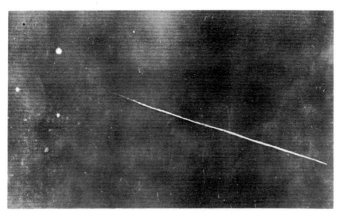

Photograph of Sputnik II taken at the Tsetsingshan Observatory, Nanking, China. (Hsinhua Agency)

THE PRECISION TRACKING PROGRAM

Early in the preparations for the International Geophysical Year it was realized that, if satellites are to be a really dependable tool in the study of the upper atmosphere and geodetic conditions, a tracking device of a precision never before obtained must be developed. The problem was turned over to Dr. James G. Baker (previously famous for his development of the Baker-Schmidt telescope), who designed an optical system for a camera capable of detecting the flight of a golf ball sixty miles away. Dr. Baker's optics were incorporated in a mounting originated by Joseph Nunn of Los Angeles, and the completed instrument more than met what had been considered "impossible" precision requirements.

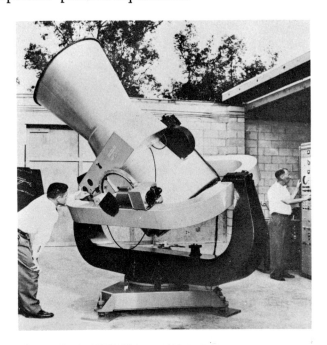

Two views of the giant Baker - Nunn satellite-tracking camera. These are the most efficient cameras in the world for photographing the satellites. They are 10 feet high and 8 feet wide. (Courtesy Smithsonian Astrophysical Observatory)

The timing arrangement is one of the most remarkable features of the instrument. This is a crystal-controlled clock which includes a rotating dial for 1/100-second intervals and a circular-sweep oscilloscope which can be read to 1/10,000 second. When the clock readings are checked against the time signals of WWV, themselves a marvel of precise timing, the total error in timing is less than 1/1000 second.

The camera is designed to have a field of view 2.5° wide on each side of the satellite's path and 30° long in the direction of its motion. It uses film 55 mm wide and a foot long which, with the 16-inch focal length of the optics, produces a measuring error of 2 seconds of arc. This is less than the width of a strip of sky cut off by the width of a pin held at arm's length. There are two shutters, one a barrel-shaped arrangement with two "staves" missing, which break the path of the satellite into timed segments, and the other a clamshell cover which opens and closes to start and stop the exposure. The two shutters work so smoothly that from 10 to 100 photographs can be taken each time a satellite passes.

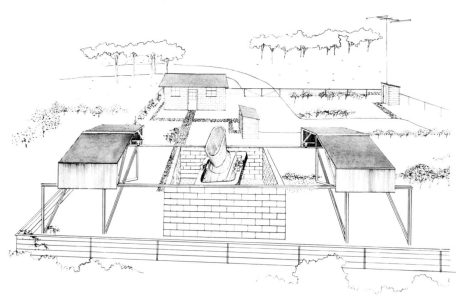

This is the way the Baker-Nunn cameras are set up at the observing stations. (Courtesy Smithsonian Astrophysical Observatory)

The production of these cameras represents a nationwide cooperative effort. The optical components were made in Norwalk, Connecticut, from glass produced in West Germany and Corning, New York. The clocks came from Williams Bay, Wisconsin, and the assembling of the mechanical structures was done at South Pasadena, California.

Two Baker-Nunn cameras are located in the United States, while 10 more are placed at strategic points all over the world. They are located in South Africa, Hawaii, Japan, Curaçao (Dutch West Indies), Spain, Iran, Peru, India, Argentina, and Australia. The distance between each of these stations has been measured to an accuracy of 30 feet, which means that the path of the satellites measured by them can be computed to the same accuracy.

This gigantic system of precision tracking stations is now in full operation, so that no satellite may circle the earth without full information about its orbit becoming known to the watchers below. The Moonwatch program, as a means of tracking satellites, is becoming obsolete, and its members are concentrating mostly on what the organization was originally created for, observing the births and deaths of satellites.

hotograph of 1958 alpha (Explorer I) ᴋen with the Baker-Nunn camera at Or-an, New Mexico. The satellite appears as ᴇe three lines of dots ascending in the ᴇenter of the photograph. The horizontal ᴀashed lines are star traces. The time inter-al between exposures is 8 seconds; each xposure is 1.6 seconds. (Courtesy Smith-ᴏnian Astrophysical Observatory)

This is one of the first satellite photographs taken with the Ba-ker-Nunn camera. It shows Sput-nik I as it appeared over Pasa-dena, California, October 23, 1957. Can you read the time shown on the clock? (Courtesy Smithsonian Astrophysical Ob-servatory)

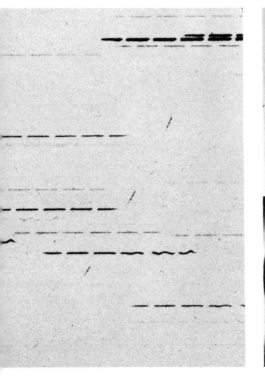

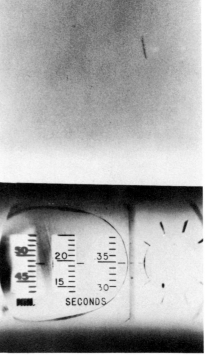

Chapter **7**

Why the Satellites?

So far we have talked about the characteristics of the orbits of satellites, the ways and means of launching them, and how to find them after they are launched. But, except for passing references, we have ignored their real purpose. Why are they in the sky? Why should nations like the United States and Soviet Russia spend millions of dollars to put them there?

An early assumption was that they are merely testing devices for military weapons. It was considered reasonable that if a satellite could be launched with the precision necessary to place it in orbit, an operation where the smallest error means failure, other missiles capable of hitting earth targets with precision were available. Actually, this is only part of the truth because long-range missiles, such as the Intercontinental Ballistic Missiles, have few elements in common with satellite launchings except, of course, the propulsion system itself.

The fact is that satellites are designed for one specific purpose only: they are tools of pure research. Their findings have little to do with military developments. The satellites are explorers of the final frontier, an area defined as beginning at 100 miles above the earth and having no external limit. This area had been probed with balloons, with high-flying aircraft, and with instrumented rockets. But none of these was a device that could bring back, or send back, really adequate information, since none could go far enough or stay up long enough to do it. An instrument was needed that could probe all levels up to and beyond the limits of our atmosphere. Satellites satisfy all requirements, and the money and time spent on them have already paid generous dividends in information returned.

Characteristics of the First Six Satellites

Satellite	Launching Date	Weight (lbs.)	Type	Perigee (miles)	Apogee (miles)	Period (minutes)	Inclination of orbit
Sputnik I (1957 alpha 2)	Oct. 4, 1957		sphere	140	589	96.2	65.3°
Carrier for Sputnik I (1957 alpha 1)	Oct. 4, 1957	6,118 (est.) 7,040 (est.)	cone	140	589	96.2	65.3°
Sputnik II (1957 beta)	Nov. 3, 1957	184	cone	149	1,035	103.7	65.4°
Explorer I (1958 alpha)	Feb. 1, 1958	31	cylinder	229	1,578	114	33.1°
Vanguard I (1958 beta 2)	Mar. 17, 1958	3	sphere	405	2,463	134.3	34.3°
Rocket for Vanguard I (1958 beta 1)	Mar. 17, 1958	51	cylinder	405	2,463	134.3	34.3°
Explorer III (1958 gamma)	Mar. 26, 1958	31	cylinder	117	1,740	115.9	33.5°
Sputnik III° (1958 delta 2)	May 15, 1958	2,925	cone	123	1,160	105.8	64.9°
Rocket for Sputnik III (1958 delta 1)	May 15, 1958	?	cylinder	123	1,160	105.8	64.9°

° There are also two other small components of Sputnik III, thought to be parts of the shielding device of the nose cone.

What must be learned about the final frontier before we can venture into it? What are the real conditions in the upper reaches of the atmosphere and how do those conditions influence the lower atmosphere and the earth itself? The list of problems is long and impressive; it is worth our while to consider at least a part of it.

A. AIR DENSITY

Very little is known about the atmosphere above an altitude of 100 miles. Some scientists think there is no atmosphere at all above 1,500 miles, while others think it reaches all the way to the sun. One of the latest ideas for space travel is to obtain power from the oxygen atoms (which are supposed to exist in space) by using devices to produce energy from the unification of the atoms into molecules. But one of the concepts of the upper atmosphere upon which everyone agrees is that beyond 250 miles there are few particles, so few, in fact, that one of them would have to travel over five miles before colliding with another. (In contrast, at the surface of the earth the distance between molecules is only 1/10,000 of a millimeter.) At

Information Derived from the Satellites

What we have already learned from the satellites:

1. Newly discovered radiation at the 600-mile level.
2. The satellites can be satisfactorily insulated to protect their contents (humans, animals, or instruments) from the extremes of temperature found in space.
3. The meteorite hazard is not as great as previously assumed.
4. Cosmic radiation is only 12 times that found at sea level—much below what was expected.
5. The density of the atmosphere is much greater than expected—up to 14 times at some levels.

What we hope the satellites will tell us.

1. The nature and origin of the newly discovered radiation.
2. How the earth's heat balance is affected by happenings on the sun.
3. How much energy is possessed by ultraviolet radiation.
4. The factors which influence the earth's magnetic field.
5. The circulation in the upper atmosphere.
6. The cause of the aurora.
7. The true nature of the ionosphere and the factors which affect it.
8. Physical characteristics of our own planet.

lesser heights of 100 miles, however, there are enough air molecules to slow down a satellite and cause it to burn up. Sputnik II, for example, was traveling at this height just before its fiery plunge into the Caribbean.

A light satellite is retarded more than a heavy one of equal size, since collision with air particles will have more effect on the light one. A good parallel is the relative distances a golf ball and a Ping-Pong ball will travel if each is thrown with the same force. If we wish to measure air density by means of a satellite, we need no instruments in it. Launching it, then waiting to see what happens when it spirals toward the earth will give us a great deal of information about the density of the levels through which it travels. The lighter and larger the satellite, the more closely we can observe it, since it is more sensitive to different air densities.

Such launchings are definitely planned as part of the IGY program. The vehicles used will be spheres of plastic, inflated after they are placed in orbit, and they will range in size from 30 inches to 12 feet in diameter. Their orbits may depart from the usual American pattern in that they may travel farther to the north and south. Since they will not be instrumented, there is no gain in confining them to a path that must pass over the radio fence set up 35° on each side of the equator to receive signals.

Much has been learned already about the thickness of the atmosphere from satellites already launched. As a result scientists are revising some of their previous values. The early satellites showed, for example, that air density in the upper atmosphere is about fourteen times more than had been previously supposed.

B. TEMPERATURE

In spite of the vast amount that has been written in recent months, many people still hold incorrect conceptions about space temperatures. The "coldness of the void" is a misconception hard to get rid of. Actually, the air molecules of the outer atmosphere have a high temperature. At 250 miles, the temperature may be as high as 2,500° F., but this does not mean that a man in a space suit will be immediately cooked. We must remember that these "hot" molecules are five miles apart, and that the space in between them is neither hot nor cold; it simply has no temperature. If this seems hard to believe, we must remember that temperature, as physicists conceive of it, is a measure of the energy possessed by moving particles. Therefore, in places where there are no particles, there can be no temperature. On the other hand, if our space-suited human is in the shadow of the earth, he will tend to cool off, but even here the cooling will be a slow process. We learned in high school physics that heat may be transferred in three ways; by conduction, convection, or radiation. The first two simply do not exist in space. Conduction, of course, implies that there must be two objects of different heat content, and a conducting material in between to transfer the heat from one to the other. In space, there is no conducting material along which the heat can travel. And since there are no air currents, losing heat by convection is equally impossible. Our man will radiate away some of his body heat, but if we line the inside of his suit with some reflective material, he will remain warm in the same way as coffee inside a thermos bottle.

When he is in direct sunlight (if he is circling the earth he will alternate between shadow and sunlight), he will be hot on the side next the sun and cold on the other. In fact, there may be several hundred degrees difference. This could be prevented, or at least ameliorated, by covering the outside of his suit with bands of conductive material.

Explorer I was designed to check this theory, among other things, and somewhat the same means described above were used to maintain a heat balance. Its radio sent back the reassuring news that the internal temperature remained within a range of 32° to 108° F., a variation comparable to an unheated house in Florida.

Both internal and external satellite temperatures are measured by thermistors (devices that convert temperature conditions into minute electric currents) located inside the instrument package and on the outer shell. Spherical satellites have two external thermistors, one located at the equator of the spinning ball and the other near one of the poles. A point on the equator of the ball constantly changes position relative to the sun, while one located near the pole is almost motionless in this respect. Thus two temperature ranges are measured.

C. METEORITE MEASUREMENT

Approximately 7½ billion meteorites strike the earth's atmosphere in any 24-hour period. They range from the size of a fine dust particle to half an inch in diameter. A very few are larger—some as much as twenty tons. But the greater part of them are tiny particles whose most impressive characteristic is the brilliant streak of incandescent gas they leave behind when they enter the atmosphere at the incredible speeds at which they travel. A meteorite as small as a grain of sand will pile up air molecules in front of it. These molecules are buffeted until they become very hot, and they will continue to glow as they are left behind the speeding meteorite. The tiniest meteorites (fine dust particles, or micrometeorites, which outnumber all the rest) do not produce enough light to be seen from the earth.

Of this huge 24-hour-deluge of meteorites, only about 30,000 are as large and heavy as a United States nickel. Even this sounds like a dangerously large number to someone who wishes to venture out into the area above the protective blanket of atmosphere. A five-cent piece, traveling at a rate of 25 miles a second, will penetrate just about anything that gets in its way.

At this point, most of us would decide to stay on earth. Yet, if we analyze these figures, we find there is very little danger. Thirty thousand meteorites, spread over an area as large as the earth's surface, is an extremely sparse concentration. The chance of one's striking any given square mile of the earth is only 1 in 6,000, which makes the chance of a satellite's being hit practically zero, even if the satellite is very large. Put in another way, an object with a surface area of 1,000 square feet, orbiting in the vicinity of the earth, would be struck by a meteorite of this size once every 24,000 years.

But we have been talking only of large meteorites. Any object traveling around the earth for a 24-hour period is bound to be hit by many micrometeorites during that time. Satellites carry several measuring devices to find out how many of these collisions take place and how damaging they are likely to be. The Explorers have a grid, which is stretched on the outside of the vehicle, made up of twelve fine wires connected to an electric circuit in parallel. Whenever one of these wires is broken, the event is recorded on the inside instruments as a change in the resistance of the system. In spite of the fact that early in the flight of Explorer I three of these wires were broken, the instrument package of the satellite continued to work normally, indicating that the damage to the satellite itself was slight.

Meteorite impact is also registered by small erosion gauges, consisting of thin film resistors coating a piece of glass attached to the outer surface of the satellite. Meteorites wear away the film by a sand-blasting action, and the change of resistance shows on the gauge. Another arrangement substitutes a cadmium sulfide detector for the erosion gauge. An opaque paint covers the light-sensitive cadmium sulfide. Each meteorite impact chips the paint enough to expose some of the chemical to the light, and a signal of increasing strength, as more paint is worn away, is recorded.

Mounting sensitive microphones on the outside of the satellite is the most direct way of recording meteorite impacts. The microphones are hooked to a counting system, which makes it possible to keep an accurate record of the number of collisions during any given period.

These devices record only tiny particles, or micrometeorites, that strike the satellite. A double shell covering, or annulus, arranged in a doughnut-like ring under the skin of the satellite supplies information about the damage caused by larger meteorites. A gas under low pressure fills the annulus. Any object large enough to penetrate the outer shell makes a hole proportional to its size. The rate at which the gas escapes shows approximately how large the hole is.

So far in the history of satellites, danger from meteorites has not appeared. But we need more information before this particular hazard of space can be discounted.

D. COSMIC PARTICLES

The term "cosmic ray," frequently heard, is a misnomer, for they are not rays, but particles. Most of them are the nuclei of hydrogen or helium atoms or, in the case of the most powerful type, of metallic atoms (the nucleus of an atom is what is left after the outer shells of light electrons have been stripped away). These particles travel with energies far surpassing anything that can be produced by the most powerful atom-smashers on earth. They streak toward our atmosphere from outer space; and, as they strike air molecules in the upper reaches of the atmosphere, the impact creates a number of new cosmic particles. In order to distinguish between them, we call the original particles *primaries;* and the subsidiary particles, which also have tremendous energies, we call *secondaries.* These are all charged particles and are therefore influenced by the earth's magnetic field, which tends to pull them toward the poles. Because their paths are bent in this way, it is impossible to say where the cosmic particles originate. Some authorities think they come from the sun and are produced there by solar flares, others think they have traveled through space from other galaxies.

In spite of their deflection by the magnetic field of the earth, and their absorption by the atmosphere, both types of cosmic particles get through to the earth's surface, although in relatively small concentrations. This is all to the good as far as we are concerned, for they are extremely damaging to human tissues. If they are present in large quantities above the shielding atmosphere, man will venture into that region at his peril. Shielding the occupants of a spaceship from cosmic particles is almost impossible: the amount of shielding required for safety would make the ship impossibly heavy, and anything less than that would serve only as a source of secondary cosmic particles blasted from the shielding by the terrific impact of the primaries. The extent of cosmic-particle damage to humans is still speculative. There is reason to believe they affect reproductive cells more than other parts of the body; thus the effect of exposure to large numbers of them may not be known until several generations have passed. Extensive experiments have been carried out with mice and other small animals, with inconclusive results. The mice who traveled in the famous sky-hook experiment (where a rocket fired from a balloon penetrated several thousand miles into space before returning to earth) showed no ill effects other than patches of white hair where, it was assumed, they had been struck by primary cosmic particles.

Satellites are ideal vehicles for cosmic-particle experiments. Equipped with Geiger counters, they send back precise information on cosmic-particle intensity. Information collected so far in the satellite program indicates that the intensity is not as great as scientists had anticipated. As a matter of fact, in the nearer reaches of space (200 to 300 miles), cosmic radiation is only about twelve times that at sea level. This, according to Dr. William Pickering, director of the Jet Propulsion Laboratory at California Institute of Technology, is not a formidable increase. But in this area, as in that of the meteorites, much more information must be gathered before any final assumptions can be made about the safety of space.

IONOSPHERIC MEASUREMENTS

Starting at about 45 miles above the earth and extending upward to well over 200 miles, the ionosphere is a series of layers of partially ionized (electrically charged) gas particles. These strata have been studied for years because they are responsible for the reflection of radio waves and make possible the reception of long-distance broadcasts.

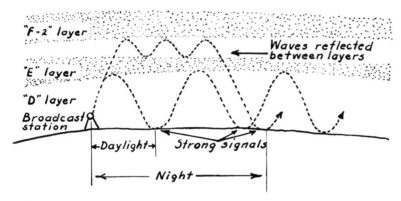

Radio waves and the ionosphere. Bouncing of radio waves between earth and ionosphere makes long-distance reception possible.

The bottom, or D, layer lies between 45 and 60 miles and has a low concentration of free electrons as well as the partially ionized gas particles mentioned above. (Electrons are negatively charged particles so light that they weigh only about 1/2000 as much as an atom.) Above the D layer, and in order of increasing electron intensity, lies the E layer (60 to 90 miles above the earth), the F layer (up to 150 miles), and the F-2 layer (up to about 200 miles). If these layers were fixed in position and concentration, they would act as consistently in reflecting radio signals as a smooth wall does in returning a tennis ball. But they vary constantly and sometimes unaccountably, and the consequence is that radio signal propagation is sometimes blacked out completely. Two influences that cause these variations are cosmic particles and the particles thrown out by the sun in its periodic upheavals, but there are probably others as well.

If the exact nature and source of the ionospheric fluctuations could be discovered, communications men could adjust existing radio transmitters and receivers to balance them.

Here again, the satellite serves as an excellent means of investigation. Its transmitters, sometimes above and sometimes below the higher strata of the ionosphere, direct radio waves against and through them from all angles. Except for brief studies made by instrumented rockets and balloons, studies of the ionosphere had to be made from the ground, a situation similar to attempting to test the strength of the roof of a building by looking at it from inside. Already much work has been done on the basis of information gathered from the transmissions of early satellites; and, although many of the effects are still not understood, their full explanation now seems only a matter of time.

This is one instance in which the dollar cost of satellites may be returned in full measure. If an investment in a few of them provides the means of improving the services of the multi-million-dollar communications industry, it is certainly money well spent.

F. THE SUN'S RADIATIONS

The light that reaches us from the sun is only a small sector of the wide band, or spectrum, of radiation originating there. On one side of this sector are the long-wave-length radio and infrared waves, and on the other are the shorter ultraviolet rays and X rays. We are interested in all these wave lengths, but chiefly in the ultraviolet and X radiation. It has been difficult, in the past, to measure this type of radiation, since much of it is absorbed in the upper atmosphere.

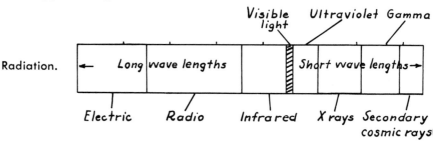

Radiation is a key area of study, especially the relationships of these radiations to solar flares, those great flaming protuberances which climb for thousands of miles above the sun's surface in only a few minutes. Whenever a solar flare takes place, the result is a terrific blast of radiation which affects the earth's magnetic field and the ionosphere. Repercussions in the lower atmosphere, caused by these blasts, probably affect our weather. The great advantage of space measurements of these phenomena is that the radiations can be investigated before they enter the earth's atmosphere.

The satellites have already reported some rather disturbing information concerning radiation. The Geiger counters carried by both Explorers (I and III) have indicated counts of up to 35,000 per second at heights above

00 miles (normal count near sea level: 30 per second). The radiation was so intense the Geiger counters "choked up," that is, they stopped registering as they passed the 600-mile mark and started again only when they swung back toward the earth. Consequently the 35,000 counts per second is an estimated, rather than an exact, figure. Radiation counts such as these mean that a man in a satellite would receive his maximum weekly exposure in a little less than 5 hours. How far out into space this belt of intensive radiation extends is a matter of conjecture, but it may go as far as 8,000 miles.

Even so, man is not necessarily excluded from this area. Properly protected with a shield that can be lighter than the cosmic-particle shield, he could pass through it with little danger. On the other hand, inhabitants of a space station orbiting above 600 miles would be continually exposed to radiation far beyond the limits now considered safe.

The study of this belt of radiation will be an important function of any future satellite, since the information sent back by the Explorers is a new and unexpected discovery.

The year 1957-1958 was chosen for an International Geophysical Year because it is a peak year for sunspot activity, and many of the fields of study were aimed specifically at correlating the happenings on the sun with subsequent events on the earth and in its atmosphere. Sunspot activity reaches a peak every eleven years; thus the IGY could be chosen well ahead of time.

Each satellite to date has carried equipment to measure the ultraviolet rays at a wave length called the Lyman-Alpha line. This particular wave length was chosen because it represents a large part of the total ultraviolet radiation received from the sun. The equipment consists of a small chamber filled with nitric oxide, a gas sensitive to this type of radiation. An electrometer tube measures the reactions in the chamber and transmits peak readings to a memory unit, where they are stored for later radio transmission to the earth. Since the ultraviolet rays travel in straight lines (as do those of visible light), measurements of their intensity will vary with the direction in which the satellite is pointing at any given time. The direction of the sun from the satellite is indicated by a gadget called an aspect cell, which contains the light-sensitive element silicon. Coupled with the Lyman-Alpha indicator, the aspect cell shows whether the indicator was turned toward the sun at the time the reading was made.

G. GEODETIC MEASUREMENTS

Although we have lived on our planet for a great many centuries, we still are not certain about just where things are on it. We have come to be fairly certain about the location of points on the continents, for by setting

up fixed points and measuring from them we can determine other geo
graphical locations to within a few feet. But this is very difficult in ocean
areas, since the points from which we measure are so far apart. Some is
lands, for example, may be thousands of feet or even several miles from the
places where our charts show them to be.

But a moving point is just as good as a fixed one for survey purposes i
we know exactly at what speed and in what direction the point is moving
By means of the marvelous Baker-Nunn cameras, a satellite can be used as a
fixed point for any moment of time, and two observers can find their dis
tances from one another by simultaneous observations, as shown by the
diagram. In this way, the world can be remapped by pooling the results of
many observations, and really accurate measurements of its surface will be
come possible.

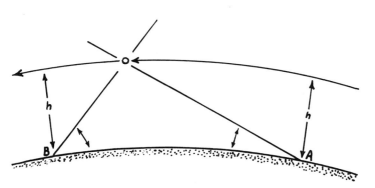

If observers at
and B measure the
angle at which the
satellite is seen fly
ing at a known
height, h, the dis
tance AB can be
found.

We are also not sure of the exact shape of our planet. We know that i
has a bulge around the equator and that it is slightly flattened at the poles
and we have an approximate idea of how great these deformations are. Bu
we cannot be sure of latitude and longitude scales until we know exactly
what the variations are. A high-flying satellite is astonishingly sensitive to
slight deformities in the earth's surface; and, by measuring the perturbation
in the satellite's orbit, we can find out the location as well as the extent of
these bulges and flattenings. This information will supplement similar find
ings determined by other means, and the final result will be a very complete
picture of all aspects of the globe upon which we live.

We shall also learn more about the interior of the earth. The materia
beneath the earth's crust is apparently not homogeneous. If it were, gravi
tational influences would be the same all over the surface, with the excep
tion of deviations resulting from its shape. These gravitational variation
also cause perturbations in the orbit of a satellite, the extent of which is a
key to locating the denser sections of the earth's interior.

4.   THE EARTH'S MAGNETIC FIELD

Surrounding the earth in lines of force running from pole to pole at vast distances above its surface, the earth's magnetic field protects us from the onslaught of cosmic particles and other charged particles from space. For the most part, it is stable and unchanging over long periods of time, but occasionally it undergoes rapid variations. Analysis of these variations shows that their main features might be produced by three great electrical currents of hundreds of thousands of amperes in the upper atmosphere. These great currents travel through the extremely rarefied gases of the upper reaches of the atmosphere just as smaller currents pass across the comparable vacuum in a radio tube. Two of these currents seem to be located in the zones where the northern and southern lights occur, and the third is a belt of great intensity, only a few hundred miles wide, which surrounds the magnetic equator. Proof of the existence of these currents, their nature, and their cause is an intriguing problem which has considerable priority in the IGY program. The magnetic field variations seem to have some effect on the ionosphere layers and on the weather, for it is suspected that they cause ionized air to circulate in very strong wind systems in the lower atmosphere.

The earth's magnetic field for each 10° of latitude. The heavy circle is the ionosphere. The length of the longest ellipse shown is 35,000 miles. (From *IGY Bulletin*; used by permission of USNC-IGY)

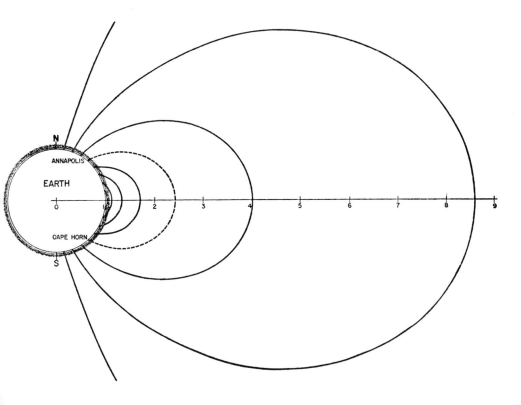

Like so many other aspects of the atmosphere, the disturbances of the magnetic field increase and decrease with the number of sunspots, which is considered adequate proof that the spots are caused by bursts of radiation from the sun. The disturbances can be measured from stations set up near the poles and around the magnetic equator. They can also be investigated by satellites carrying magnetometers into the regions where the great currents are thought to exist, and also by inflatable, uninstrumented satellites whose behavior will yield information about the strength of the magnetic fields through which they pass.

Any conductor placed in a magnetic field will behave according to the strength and variations of that field. This is, of course, the principle of the electric motor, where the movement of the armature is determined by the varying magnetic fields set up by the field coils. The same principle will influence a metal-surfaced satellite which, if set spinning in the earth's magnetic field, will vary its rate of spin according to the forces acting upon it.

I. WEATHER STUDIES

Some of the factors influencing the weather have already been mentioned. The forces set in motion in the upper atmosphere by solar activity are sooner or later translated into forces which influence the lower levels. How this translation takes place will become known when more is understood about the nature of the original forces. It must, of course, be the result of many influences and is not a problem that will be solved immediately. Perhaps because the weather is a subject close to the hearts of many of us, we are likely to make snap judgments about it on the basis of insufficient evidence. We remember, for example, that the winters of 1947 and 1958 were each marked by great sunspot activity, heavy snows, and cold weather. It might seem an inescapable conclusion that sunspots and chilblains are somehow connected. It would be convenient if cause-and-effect weather relationships were as simple as this, but the truth seems to be that the problem is extremely complex and that years of study of all levels of the atmosphere must be made if we are to obtain a clear picture of its nature.

In one area, however, there is great hope for long-range weather forecasting. The earth receives a daily amount of heat from the sun and in turn radiates an equal amount into space, thus maintaining what is called the *heat balance*. But minute variations in the balance occur from day to day. Studies of these variations have shown that there is a relationship between the amount of heat received from the sun and temperature patterns on the earth measured several days later. Now, if the problem can be attacked on a large enough scale, it is possible that the law of variation of the sun's heat may be discovered. If this happens, we can predict the heat to be received for a month or a year ahead, and make long-range weather forecasts based on it.

The satellite is the ideal instrument for such a study. It can measure the sun's heat by means of one set of instruments, and the earth's radiated heat with another set. These will be continuous and uninterrupted measurements, capable of accumulating a great deal of data over a period of time. The end result may be the greatest contribution to meteorology since man first became interested in the weather.

In the meantime, the satellites can help us extend our short-range forecasting by reporting on cloud layers and general atmospheric conditions. Concentrations of clouds reflect more light than the earth below. A simple photoelectric cell placed in a satellite to measure reflected light would indicate the extent of the cloud pattern below it. The most perceptive instrument would be a television camera which could report the weather disturbance all around the earth every hundred minutes or so. As a device to report on the progress of a large-scale disturbance such as a tropical hurricane, a satellite would have no equal.

J. PHOTOGRAPHY

The atmosphere obscures our view of other heavenly bodies to the same extent that a dirty windowpane distorts and conceals landscape details. We can never know very much about the planets until we push a camera outside the shifting and quivering air masses that surround us. Once this is accomplished, many of the questions about our solar-system neighbors which have long been the subject of contentious argument (the Martian "canals," for example, or the nature of the cover of clouds over Venus) will be resolved to our satisfaction. Solar photography may give us really definite information about the surface of the sun. Are sunspots "islands of intense calm floating in the otherwise turbulent sea of the sun's atmosphere," as Dr. Menzel of Harvard Observatory suggests, or do they conform more to the ideas of Dr. A. H. Shapley, who describes them as "centers of swirling gases and intense magnetic fields"? These and many other unresolved questions depend on a clearer picture of our surroundings than we can obtain from the earth's surface.

Equipping a satellite with a television camera involves formidable technicalities, but no more so than many other of the instrumentation problems that are already solved. The reward for the effort may be a new understanding of the details of the solar system, and, if the camera is turned toward the earth, a new insight into some of our own terrestrial problems.

K. OTHER AREAS FOR SATELLITE STUDY

Every major field of science has aspects that can be studied best with the help of satellites, and the requests which have been presented to the U.S. National Committee for the IGY are almost numberless. Each area of study requires its own specific instrumentation and increases the complexity of the "packaging" problem inside the satellite. Selecting those which should have priority is a problem which calls for the wisdom of a scientific Solomon. Let us consider one or two that, while they seem to have little pragmatic value, are still of intense interest to most of us because of their bearing on the "how and why" of the universe itself.

The Einstein Clock. One of the implications of the Relativity Theory is that if two clocks are placed in vehicles moving at different speeds, the clock in the swifter vehicle will run slower than the other. A clock on the earth, while moving swiftly in many directions at once (motion from the earth's rotation, its revolution around the sun, the motion of the sun itself as it drags the earth behind it, and so on), is at rest relative to one placed in a 5-mile-a-second satellite. The difference in rate will be very small but it is nevertheless measurable. It is possible to produce clocks that will detect this small variation in time. The experiment would constitute one more verification of the "improbable" suppositions of the General Theory of Relativity.

An allied theory, but quite different in scope, is that the time scale of atomic phenomena is influenced by gravitational influences. According to this theory, an atomic clock at a distance of 3,000 miles from the earth would run faster than its twin on the earth. Again the difference is very small, but still measurable. Since orbits of 2,500-mile apogee have already been accomplished, the test of this theory should not be impossibly difficult if a communications system of sufficient accuracy between the earth and the satellite could be established.

The Expanding Universe. Perhaps one of the most controversial theories of recent times is Hubble's idea that the universe is expanding. All bodies in space seem to be moving away from a common point, and the farther away from this point the more rapidly they move. Hubble based his theory on the so-called red shift in their spectra, which, applied to light, has its analogy to sound in the fact that a decreasing pitch in the sound of a locomotive whistle means it is moving away from us. When the light from a star is photographed through a spectroscope, the elements that make up the star reveal themselves by lines spread across the photograph. Each of the lines represents the wave length of the light rays that come from each element, and the lines are spread out across the spectrograph in the order of their wave length. The lines on the red end of the spectrograph represent the longer wave lengths, and if all the lines are shifted from their normal position toward the red, it must mean that all wave lengths have become lengthened a little. Since the decreasing pitch in the sound of a locomotive whistle as it moves away from us indicates a longer wave length, then the stars that show this red shift must also be moving away. But the red shift is difficult to measure from the bottom of our atmosphere since it has much competition from other interfering radiations. From the unobstructed position of a satellite, however, it would no longer be in competition and should be more easily measurable.

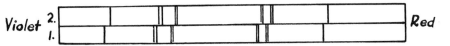

The red shift. (1) Spectral lines for an element as measured in the laboratory. (2) Same lines appearing in the light of a rapidly receding star. All lines have shifted toward the red end of the spectrum.

Solving of these and many other problems depends on sending exact information from the satellite back to earth. At present there are two ways to do this: telemetering devices which store up information by means of "memory" cells and transmit it at regular intervals, and "command units" which tape-record material and play it back upon receiving a signal from the ground.

TELEMETERED TRANSMISSIONS

What is telemetering? To most of us it is a mysterious word appearing in newspaper and magazine articles on satellites. There is no way of describing the process adequately without going into technical details which few people have the background to understand, but at least we can obtain a general idea of its operation if we cite an example of the way it might work in another field.

Let us suppose we wish to keep track of the temperature on a mountain top. We will assume that there is a supply of electric power and we can set up a radio transmitter which will operate continuously. We attach a piece of metal to the tuning knob of the transmitter in such a way that when the metal becomes warm and expands it will turn the knob to a higher frequency setting, and to a lower one when it contracts. Now we set up the thermometer, noting the frequencies which both high and low temperatures produce. From this information we make a calibration curve, which tells us the exact temperature represented by any frequency setting.

If we return to the foot of the mountain and set up a radio receiver, we can learn the temperature at the top by observing the frequency to which we must tune the receiver to pick up the signal broadcast by the transmitter.

We find that this system works so well that we wish to expand our operation by getting information on wind direction and velocity as well. We are already using the frequency range as an indicator of temperature; so, after a little thought, we decide to attach a switch to the transmitter, making the time the transmitter is in operation an indication of wind direction, and the interval between transmissions a key to wind velocity. This is a little more difficult to do, but we finally succeed in rigging up a device that operates as shown in the table here.

Temperature		Wind Velocity		Wind Direction	
Frequency	Degrees	"On" Time	m.p.h.	"Off" Time	Direction
10	40	1 sec.	10	2 sec.	north
15	60	2 sec.	20	4 sec.	east
20	80	3 sec.	30	6 sec.	south
25	100	4 sec.	40	8 sec.	west

We try the system out and receive a transmission on a dial setting of 17.5 which lasts for 3 seconds before going off the air. It comes on again after 5 seconds of silence, and we interpret the cycle as indicating 70° F., wind velocity 30 m.p.h., and wind direction southeast.

This is admittedly a crude illustration, but it is a parallel to the telemetry system in a satellite. Each transmission can broadcast data from three different instruments; the frequency of the transmission, its time, and the interval between transmissions each indicating a specific kind of measurement.

HOW SATELLITE TELEMETRY WORKS

A typical satellite telemetry encoder carries the system described into a little more complicated pattern by using several frequency ranges, or channels, and by setting up a definite sequence in which the channels will be heard.

To be a little more specific, it transmits a continuous series of high-frequency audio "bursts," or transmissions of very short duration. These bursts occur on 6 channels of different frequency ranges, the spread in each

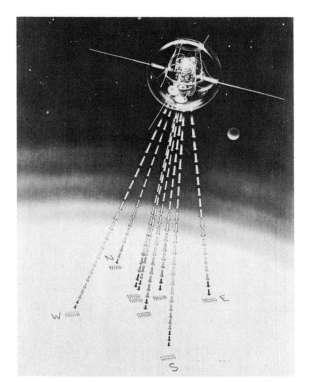

How a satellite's radio signals are transmitted to ground stations. The stations, by pooling the information concerning the direction of the satellite at the time the signals were received, can determine the satellite's position. (Bendix Radio Corporation Photo)

lying between 5 and 12.5 kilocycles. The channels always transmit in the same order, and a sequence of 16 transmissions makes up what is called a "scan" or "frame." The frequency on any one burst constitutes definite information about any single condition in the satellite, such as the inside temperature. The duration of the burst (incredibly short, ranging from 4 to 30 milliseconds) yields information about some other condition, and the interval between bursts reveals specific data about a third. Thus 48 separate information channels are provided in any one scan.

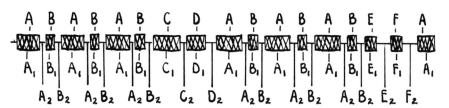

One complete transmission of telemetered information. A, B, etc.—burst frequencies. A_1, B_1, etc.—burst duration. A_2, B_2, etc.—intervals between bursts. See table on next page for information transmitted on each channel.

Telemetry Channel Assignments

Burst No.	High Frequency Burst		Burst Duration		Interval Between Bursts	
	Channel	Function	Channel	Function	Channel	Function
1	A	Instantaneous Lyman-α	A1	Polar erosion A	A2	Battery volts
2	B	Solar aspect	B1	Differential pressure	B2	Short calibrate
3	A	Instantaneous Lyman-α	A1	Polar erosion A	A2	Battery volts
4	B	Solar aspect	B1	Differential pressure	B2	Short calibrate
5	A	Instantaneous Lyman-α	A1	Polar erosion A	A2	Battery volts
6	B	Solar aspect	B1	Differential pressure	B2	Short calibrate
7	C	Meteor count, units	C1	Long calibrate	C2	Battery volts
8	D	Meteor count, tens	D1	Package temperature	D2	Polar skin temperature
9	A	Instantaneous Lyman-α	A1	Polar erosion A	A2	Battery volts
10	B	Solar aspect	B1	Differential pressure	B2	Short calibrate
11	A	Instantaneous Lyman-α	A1	Polar erosion A	A2	Battery volts
12	B	Solar aspect	B1	Differential pressure	B2	Short calibrate
13	A	Instantaneous Lyman-α	A1	Polar erosion A	A2	Battery volts
14	B	Solar aspect	B1	Differential pressure	B2	Short calibrate
15	E	Meteor count, hundreds	E1	Polar erosion B	E2	Equator skin temperature
16	F	Peak Lyman-α	F1	Equator erosion	F2	Cadmium sulfide cell

Reprinted from *IGY Bulletin,* by permission of the USNC-IGY.

This number provides more channels than there are instruments to supply information. The full-size (21-inch) Vanguard satellite, for example, sends data on only 17 conditions, including inside and outside temperatures, specific measuring devices such as the Lyman-Alpha chamber or the erosion gauges, and operating data such as battery power and calibration checks. The large number of channels makes it possible to use several of them for one specific condition. Thus meteorite impacts register on three channels, one for units, a second for tens, and a third for hundreds of impacts. The combination yields an exact count of meteorites for each scan.

A block diagram of the telemetry system used for the first US-IGY earth satellite. (From *IGY Bulletin;* used by permission of USNC-IGY)

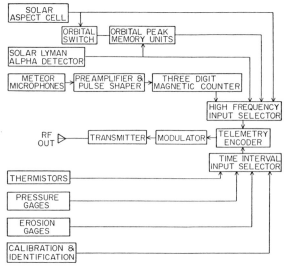

Some of the information gathered by the instruments, especially the type that records rapidly changing conditions such as the solar aspect of the spinning satellite, is transmitted as soon as it is received, while other categories are accumulated in memory units and sent at regular intervals. The tables show the kinds of data transmitted and the order in which they are sent. These represent the instrument package of a specific satellite— in this case the first fully instrumented Vanguard. Other satellites will have different packages, although any given type of instrument will be carried through a series of satellites until the data it gathers has become complete.

Model of the Vanguard satellite constructed by Walter A. Munn, Field Representative of the Smithsonian Astrophysical Observatory, for the Moonwatch program.

In this type of telemetry a constant stream of information is produced by the satellite. Unfortunately much of it is wasted, for the satellite passes over vast stretches of ocean where it is far beyond the range of the receivers for which its information is intended.

THE "COMMAND UNITS"

These are satellites whose "memories" are much longer than those carrying the telemetered units. The basic apparatus is a miniature tape recorder which weighs only half a pound. The tape moves forward at the rate of 5/1000 inch per second, and as it moves it records information from the satellite instruments. The satellite carries two radio transmitters: one of low power (10 milliwatts—a 60-watt electric light bulb uses 6,000 times as much power as this little instrument produces) which transmits on 108.00 megacycles, and one of high power (60 milliwatts), using 108.03 megacycles. The 10-milliwatt transmitter sends constant signals so ground stations may locate it, but the higher powered one transmits only when activated by signals from the ground. As the satellite approaches a ground station that sends the coded signal for it to transmit, the tape reverses and feeds its information into the transmitter. The whole operation lasts only five seconds, after which the freshly erased tape once more starts to store up information. This has proved very successful in the Explorer III satellite for obtaining and transmitting cosmic-particle information, and undoubtedly will be part of the packaging for many future satellites. Its only disadvantage is that, if the stored-up information is not received at the time of transmission, it is lost forever. There is also the possibility that the instrument may be "milked" of its information if the signal to transmit is sent accidentally.

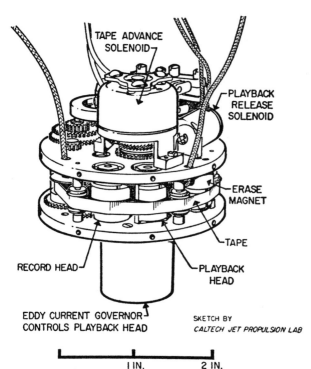

TAPE ADVANCE SOLENOID

PLAYBACK RELEASE SOLENOID

ERASE MAGNET

TAPE

RECORD HEAD

PLAYBACK HEAD

EDDY CURRENT GOVERNOR CONTROLS PLAYBACK HEAD

SKETCH BY CALTECH JET PROPULSION LAB

1 IN.   2 IN.

The tape recorder used in Explorer III (1958 gamma). (From *IGY Bulletin*; used by permission of USNC-IGY)

Chapter **8**

ooking Ahead

The names of the early American satellites—"Explorer," "Vanguard"—symbolize their purpose. They represent the first "voyages," as it were, in the most dramatic and important explorations yet undertaken by man.

These early satellites will be followed by ever larger and more complex ones before the first manned vehicles take off for outer space. Why so many? Because, as we saw in the last chapter, there is so much to learn about space. An individual satellite reports upon relatively few of the fields where man seeks knowledge, and this information must be repeatedly checked before it can be synthesized into an orderly picture of space conditions.

So there will be many satellites, the final number limited only by their expense. Since they will be more highly instrumented, and therefore larger, we shall be able to see and track them easier.

Size is one of the most important characteristics of any satellite. The 6-inch Vanguard I was a notable achievement from the point of view of placing a satellite in orbit and as a testing device for solar batteries, but its tiny size limited its instruments to radios and simple temperature devices. This "baby" will be followed into space by satellites weighing from 500 pounds to 3 tons. In fact, the latter figure may be the rule instead of the exception.

The growth rate of satellites is well demonstrated by the first three Russian Sputniks: Sputnik 1, 184 pounds; Sputnik II, ½ ton; Sputnik III, 1½ tons. From studies made of the rate of descent of Sputnik II, the original figure of 1,120 pounds has been expanded to over 7,000 pounds, but this includes the third-stage rocket as well as the satellite proper.

The Jupiter-C Rocket at Cape Canaveral, Florida, launching the first US-IGY satellite—1958 alpha, or Explorer I—at 10:48 P.M. E.S.T., January 31, 1958. Below is a drawing of the satellite it put in orbit. (Official U.S. Army photographs)

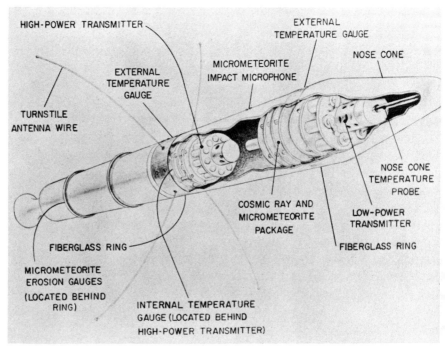

HIGH-POWER TRANSMITTER

EXTERNAL TEMPERATURE GAUGE

EXTERNAL TEMPERATURE GAUGE

MICROMETEORITE IMPACT MICROPHONE

NOSE CONE

TURNSTILE ANTENNA WIRE

NOSE CONE TEMPERATURE PROBE

COSMIC RAY AND MICROMETEORITE PACKAGE

LOW-POWER TRANSMITTER

FIBERGLASS RING

FIBERGLASS RING

MICROMETEORITE EROSION GAUGES (LOCATED BEHIND RING)

INTERNAL TEMPERATURE GAUGE (LOCATED BEHIND HIGH-POWER TRANSMITTER)

Launching Vanguard I at Cape Canaveral, Florida, at 7:16 A.M. E.S.T., March 17, 1958. (Official U.S. Navy photograph)

Sputnik III (1958 Delta) is a good example of the increasing complexity of satellite instrumentation. Its 200 cubic feet of space provides room for three sets of instruments. One set observes solar radiation, cosmic rays, and meteorites; another measures composition, temperature, and pressure of the atmosphere as well as ionization in the ionosphere. The third set includes radio transmitters, devices for monitoring the first two sets, and apparatus for regulating temperatures within the satellite. Like its predecessors, the third Russian satellite has a comparatively short life expectancy—probably about six months.

But perhaps the most interesting aspect of Sputnik III is its power; the half million pounds of thrust used to place it in orbit could have propelled a lighter satellite all the way to the moon.

Some of the satellites we launch today will be watched a hundred years hence by our descendants. Even this may be a conservative estimate of their possible life span. Dr. John P. Hagen, director of Project Vanguard, thinks Vanguard I will be circling the earth 200 years from now. In fact, we can figure the lifetime of any satellite, launched with a perigee of more than 400 miles, in centuries rather than in years.

What will the new satellites look like? Except for several notable examples, after the remaining Vanguards are launched, few will be spherical. We spoke, in the last chapter, about the 12-foot inflatable spheres designed for studies of air density and the earth's magnetic field, and it is possible that several of these may be sent aloft. If the recommendations of the National Advisory Committee on Aeronautics are accepted, there will be at least one satellite whose diameter will be, not 12 feet, but *100* feet. Like its smaller prototypes, this will be a plastic balloon covered with glittering aluminum. Inflated by a small gas cartridge once it is in orbit, this type of satellite would not collapse from meteorite punctures. It should hold its shape indefinitely since there is no outside air pressure to act on it. Even though there will be insufficient air to collapse this giant satellite, it will be extremely sensitive to the few air molecules encountered. This sensitivity will give watchers valuable information about small differences in air density. But whatever its value in this respect, one thing is certain; it will be a spectacular sight. Here is one satellite everyone will see.

The baby inflatable balloon is tested in this vacuum chamber. This type may be launched with the Vanguards. The small gas chamber which inflates the balloon is lying on the floor of the vacuum chamber, just below the balloon. (Official USNC-IGY photograph)

Since separation of satellite and third-stage rocket adds an extra step to an already highly complicated operation, this operation may be eliminated in the new satellites. They will be instrumented third-stage rockets, large and probably easy to see. Their size will vary with their purpose. Those which carry animals for biological studies require much extra space for protective devices, for food, and for extra instruments to observe animal reactions to space conditions.

The long "count down" which now adds so much to the drama of a satellite launching may eventually be a thing of the past. Liquid fuels, with their many difficulties and dangers, will probably become as outdated as the acetylene lamps which a generation ago were used to light our automobiles. Solid fuels, once considered too intractable for the initial propellant and therefore relegated to the final rocket stages, are now beginning to replace the cumbersome liquid-fuel combinations. They are already used in the Navy's Polaris missile and the newly developed Minuteman of the Air Force, a three-stage, 57-foot monster which packs enough wallop to put a satellite into orbit.

Solid fuels possess several advantages. They are easily handled and can be stored for long periods of time without deterioration. More important, however, is the weight saved in the construction of rockets. In these rockets the intricate pumps and complex plumbing details required for liquid fuels are almost completely eliminated. Nevertheless, liquid fuels will be useful for years to come for many purposes. The moonshots, assigned to such giant ICBM's as the Thor, at present use liquid fuels for the first two stages but a solid fuel for the third.

How many more satellites shall we see in the next few years? The Porter Report[1] calls for many more during the five-year period following IGY and for an expenditure of 150 million dollars a year for satellite purposes. Nobody knows just how much it costs to put a satellite into orbit, but the expense is diminishing with improvements in fuels and launching techniques. So many million dollars, even if the cost per satellite is astronomically high, should produce many of them.

For further evidence of the growth in the launching program, we need only to look at a diagram of the Cape Canaveral installations where additional launching areas are already laid out and preparations for still more are going ahead. Not all are launching pads for satellites, but each can become one quickly. Other launching points are appearing, not only in Russia, our chief competitor in the satellite field, but all over the world.

---

[1] Recommendations of the Earth Satellite Panel of the U.S. National Committee for the International Geophysical Year in the report *Basic Objectives of a Continuing Program of Scientific Research in Outer Space.*

Let us guess, then, as a conservative estimate, that by the middle of 1958 at least thirty satellites will have been launched.

But even more exciting than the increase in number of satellites will be the expansion of their range. We may expect the most dramatic event of our century to take place—man's first physical contact with the moon. Whether or not the moon's surface can ever be useful is a matter not yet decided, but in the meantime the race for the moon is a real one.

It would be spectacular to try to place a mark on the moon's surface. Explorers always place flags on new territory, and space explorations will probably be no exception. A mark on a dark surface like the moon's would be relatively easy to produce. The moon's albedo, or reflectivity, is low compared to other members of the solar system. Made of what appears to be dark brown rock, it reflects only 7 per cent of the light it receives. If we were to fill the nose of a rocket with sodium, a light, reflective metal, it would vaporize from the heat of impact and spread over a large area, perhaps several square miles. Seen through a telescope, the spot would glitter like a silver ball on a Christmas tree.

The tremendous size of the satellite rockets may be seen in this close-up view. But the rocket that is used for a moon shot will have to be even larger than this. (Official U.S. Army photograph)

But how to get the rocket there? There are two main problems, both of which have been solved. Propulsion was the big stumbling block at first, since the thrust required to produce an elliptical orbit great enough to reach the moon far exceeds any single rocket we have at present. But there are combinations of rockets that will do the job easily, and these combinations are ready to go. The speed required is nearly 24,000 miles an hour, or very near the earth's escape velocity (see chapter 1).

Control of this speed, within close limits, is the second problem. Controls must be automatic and exact, since the least deviation will result in failure. Let us review a little to find out why.

About nine-tenths of the way to the moon, the gravitational forces of earth and moon exactly balance each other. So we must produce a flat, elliptical orbit whose apogee reaches just beyond this point. Put in another way, the apogee of any orbit is the point where the object stops going away from the parent body and starts to fall back toward it. Now if another force is encountered at this point, such as the moon's gravitational field, the object will keep on moving away from the earth and toward the new source of attraction. But the moon circles the earth constantly, like a duck flying around a building. If you want to shoot the duck, you must "lead" him a little, or shoot far enough ahead of him so he literally runs into the bullet. In the same way, a moon rocket must "lead" the moon so that when the rocket has reached its apogee, the moon is in the right place to attract it most strongly.

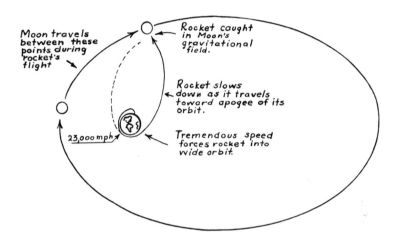

Moon shot. Moon's orbit is exaggerated.

This brings up another point some of us have difficulty understanding. If the rocket attains a speed of 24,000 miles an hour, why doesn't it go right on past the moon? The answer is that this great speed is attained only as the rocket starts out on the long leg (or toward the apogee) of its journey. Even though the gravitational field of the earth becomes weaker with distance, it is constantly pulling back on the rocket. The consequence is that, by the time the rocket reaches the balance point between earth and moon, it is practically standing still. Now if the moon is in exactly the right position at this point, it will pull the rocket down to its surface. Otherwise the rocket will go into an orbit around the moon.

This is an oversimplified version of the lunar probe, of course. Actually, the trajectory required to send a rocket to the moon successfully is an extremely complex one and the chances for failure are very high. Nevertheless, if it were considered necessary to land an object on the moon—not a safe landing, but only an impact—it could be done. Based on an initial speed of 23,827 m.p.h., the trip would take about 72 hours.

To most of us it would seem easier to hit the moon than to place an object in orbit around it, but the contrary is true. There are many possible orbits which a rocket may follow around our lunar neighbor. An object fired from earth to arrive in the moon's vicinity at approximately the right speed would fall into one of them. But to attain a lunar hit it must get there with exactly the right speed, timing, and distance from the moon's surface. On the other hand, a *permanent* orbit about the moon would be as difficult to attain as a direct hit. The greatest probability is that the rocket would orbit the moon a few times and then fly off into space. The likelihood that it would return in the direction of the earth is extremely remote.

Why do we go to this trouble? Because, although we already possess a large amount of information about our nearest neighbor in space, there is still much to learn. We should like to know what the other side of the moon is like, for nobody on earth has ever seen it. We are not sure how the moon was formed—was it once a part of our earth or did it come into being at the same time that we did? We should like to find out about the moon's magnetic field, about the composition of its surface, about the way the great craters on its surface were formed.

The satellite television cameras we spoke about in chapter 7 will soon be an actuality. When they are installed in the nose of a moon rocket, they will give us the answers to many of these questions. But to obtain complete information, we shall actually have to land there. What conditions shall we find when we do? We know already that the surface temperature on the moon varies from 212° F. (boiling point of water) when the sun is overhead at noon to 200° F. below zero at midnight. A moon day lasts two weeks, but the nights are not dark, since "earthlight" on the moon is very much stronger than moonlight on the earth. There is no air, except for very small quantities of gases oozing from the rocks. When we walk, we shall be ankle-deep in dust. We shall be pelted with tiny meteorites, burned by ultraviolet rays, constantly exposed to cosmic particles. There is no water, no vegetation, probably no living thing of any kind. Life on the Sahara is comfortable and carefree compared to that on the moon.

But before explorers attempt venturing into space as far as the moon, they must make some reconnaissance flights into nearby areas above the atmosphere. There are two possibilities for this kind of flight, each dependent upon returning through the atmosphere without burning to a crisp from the friction produced.

A space ship for these early probings might be like the X-15, a manned rocket plane capable of flying to heights of more than 100 miles, or five times the height yet attained by man. This is not true space flight, of course, since there is still some atmosphere here. Yet there is not enough air to use conventional aircraft controls. Instead, the plane will be controlled by small jets of hydrogen peroxide placed in the tail and wings. This type of space ship will glide back through the atmosphere, gaining altitude to cool off if the temperature of the control surfaces rise too high.

The next step will be taken by some successor to the X-15, which will attain orbiting speed before returning to earth. Such a craft might orbit the earth once, or even several times, before coming back.

Another idea for preliminary space flights has been suggested by Wernher von Braun, technical adviser to the Army, and the man primarily responsible for the success of the Explorer satellites. Dr. von Braun has proposed a capsule similar to that which protected the dog Laika in the second Sputnik. Researchers have found a way to keep the nose cone of a rocket from burning up on the trip back through the atmosphere. The specific details have not been released, but the main protective ingredient is a plastic that can resist terrific heat for short periods of time. If the capsule is protected by a nose cone of these properties, an animal or a man could be hurled through the atmosphere into space and then brought back safely. Dr. von Braun's idea is to try the arrangement out on monkeys before men take the perilous ride. The cost of the project is estimated at little more than the price of a single B-52; and, once the project is authorized, about a year would be required to complete it.

Once man has found that he can get out to orbiting range and return safely, the first space station can be built. True space ships must be assembled at these orbiting space stations. The reader may ask at this point, "Why not build space ships on the ground where materials are already at hand?" For the same reason that a man carries materials to the top of a hill to build a house, instead of building it in the valley and then moving it up. Another reason for space stations is that a ship could begin its journey at the velocity that the station already has in orbiting around the earth, or at about 16,000 miles an hour. Only a little additional speed is needed to escape from the gravitational pull of the earth. If the ship were to leave directly from the earth, on the other hand, it would have only the speed of the earth's rotation as an extra push—a mere 1,000 miles per hour. Finally, the earth's heavy atmosphere would greatly impede the ship's initial flight. Launching a space ship from the ground, large enough to carry men and equipment on an expedition to explore the moon, for instance, would require fuel consumption in the neighborhood of 100 tons a *second!*

The space stations will be built piecemeal from parts flown to the orbit by work crews. These man-carrying ships will be the third stages of tremendous rockets weighing over 100 tons. The first, or propelling stages, will return to earth after boosting their loads into orbit, and they will be reclaimed to deliver other sections to the orbit. For a while, the orbit level will be full of weightless hardware, but this will be collected and assembled by the work crews. The result will be a space station large enough to contain living quarters, laboratories, and work shops. As planned by Dr. von Braun, Dr. Fred Whipple, and Willy Ley, in the fascinating book *Conquest of the Moon*, this station will be a wheel-shaped structure whose diameter will be 250 feet. It will move around the earth once every two hours at a distance of 1,075 miles above sea level. The whole structure will revolve very slowly about its axis, thus creating in its occupants an artificial sensation of weight which would otherwise be absent.

While we have been discussing some of the technological problems associated with man's proposed journeys into space, we have overlooked perhaps the most important problem of all. What about his physiological responses to some of the conditions which will affect him?

One of these is the problem of weightlessness, or zero gravity. The effect of this condition on our feelings and behavior is still relatively unknown. Studies of it are inconclusive because they have to be so brief. The only way now known of producing weightlessness artificially is to dive a jet plane at great speed, then bring it up and over a "hump," as shown in the diagram. While the plane is going over the hump, the occupant has no weight. This produces the same effect, except in a more marked degree, as we all feel when we go "over the top" in a spinning ferris wheel. Because of the speed limitations of jet planes, 43 seconds has been the longest period of weightlessness so far experienced by any of the pilots. Reports on their sensations varied greatly: some became violently ill, others were highly exhilarated. These were seasoned pilots. What would have happened to the rest of us?

Another problem: what does quick acceleration do to the body? The effect of acceleration or deceleration is the reverse of weightlessness, for the body seems to weigh more. Because of inertia, objects resist speeding up or slowing down. The effect of this resistance is an apparent increase in weight—the feeling that we experience when we pass through the bottom

At very high speeds, the pilot is weightless for a few seconds as he goes over the "hump."

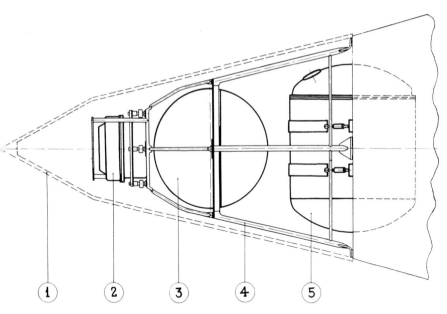

Diagram of the forward section of Sputnik II. (1) Protective nose cone jettisoned after the satellite reached its orbit. (2) Instruments for studying the sun's radiation (ultraviolet and X rays). (3) Sphere containing two radio transmitters and other instruments. (4) Frame enclosing the satellite's scientific equipment. (5) Airtight cabin for experimental dog.

Forward section of Sputnik II. (Used by permission of *USSR Magazine*)

of a "dip" in a speeding roller-coaster. At such a time we may feel twice as heavy as we ordinarily do. Pilots and physicists speak of this as twice the acceleration of gravity, or 2 g. But the rider in an ascending satellite must expect to undergo not 2 g but up to 9 g (a man weighing 180 pounds would feel as though he weighed 1,620 pounds!). Even worse, within seconds after the 9 g experience, the satellite passenger would lose all his weight (drop to zero g) and there he would remain. Human beings have been subjected to very high g values without ill effect, provided they were prepared for it. Some have repeated the experience time after time and said they didn't mind it a bit.

But in spite of these and other problems, space travel is as logical a development from its present beginnings as ordinary winged flight was from the first feeble attempts at Kitty Hawk. Most of us still have a feeling of unreality about it—we find it hard to believe that the time is nearby when man will no longer be bound to his own tiny planet.

In the meantime the flight of the satellites is followed all over the world with absorbing interest on the part of all who watch them. The excitement is the same at all stages of the life of a satellite, from the cries of "Go, baby, go!" when a rocket rises from its launching pad at Cape Canaveral to the equal excitement of a group of schoolboys as they watch a Sputnik during the final ten minutes of its life.

SATELLITES:
As Sputnik Sputtered

Peering through the dusk, a group of English astronomers at the Jodrell Bank Observatory saw it as a bright glow, more intense than the evening stars. A band of youthful Millbrook School (N.Y.) moonwatchers, camped outside their observatory, reported that it was developing a luminous tail of sparks. By the time Sputnik II flamed over the Caribbean, it was putting on a spectacular fireworks display. Finally, the Dutch tanker Mitra radioed that a "fireball with a tail of smoke and fire" was seen plunging into the sea south of the Virgin Islands.

Such was the incandescent end, last week, of the second Russian satellite. Launched Nov. 3, 1957, it carried a celebrated canine passenger, Laika. By far the most impressive of the five artificial moons which have been launched, the exact weight of Sputnik II was never known to the West, although it was thought to be 1,120 pounds.

Newsweek, April 28, 1958

Appendix I. Glossary

Achromatic objective An objective lens in a telescope or other optical instrument consisting of two kinds of glass cemented together. The second layer of glass compensates for the color error in the first.

Air density Weight of a given quantity of air compared to its volume.

Albedo The reflectivity of a heavenly body. Expressed as the ratio of light reflected to the light received from the sun. For example, the moon has an albedo of 7; 7 per cent of the light it receives is reflected.

Alcor The tiny star appearing beside Mizar at the crook in the handle of the Big Dipper.

Altair Principal star of the constellation Aquila.

Altazimuth mounting A telescope mounting in which there is free motion in two directions; horizontal (azimuth) and vertical (altitude).

Altitude The height of a heavenly body measured in degrees from the horizon.

Angular velocity Speed, expressed in degrees per second, of a body moving across the heavens.

Aperture The useful diameter of a lens.

Apogee The point in an elliptical orbit where the body is farthest from the principal focus.

Apparent field The field of the eyepiece of an optical instrument. It depends upon the field lens (the lens farthest from the eye) in the eyepiece.

Ascending node The point at which a satellite passes through the plane of the earth's equator on its journey northward.

Aspect cell A cell used to locate the direction of a body. In the case of satellites, it is used to determine the direction of the sun from the satellite.

Astronomical twilight The period, either at morning or night, when the sun is less than 18° below the horizon.

Axis The imaginary line perpendicular to the plane of revolution or rotation of a body.

Azimuth Lateral direction, measured in degrees from north clockwise around the horizon. Thus, due west has an azimuth of 270°.

Calibration   Setting up a scale reading with reference to a given fixed point.

Celestial equator   The imaginary line where the extended plane of the earth's equator cuts the heavens.

Chromatic aberration   The fault in a lens that produces colored fringes around an image.

Civil twilight   The period, either at morning or night, when the sun is less than 6° below the horizon.

Command unit   A recording unit used in satellites that will release stored-up information upon reception of a certain radio signal.

Conduction   The transfer of heat from molecule to molecule.

Constellation   A definite pattern of stars, usually representing some mythological figure, such as the constellation Hercules.

Convection   The bodily transfer of heat. Rising currents of warm air, for example, transfer heat from one place to another.

Coordinates   Lines of reference used in a graph or chart.

Cosmic particles   Particles from outer space which contain a tremendous amount of energy of motion (kinetic energy).

Declination   The position of a heavenly body measured north or south (in degrees) from the celestial equator.

Deneb   The principal star of the constellation Cygnus (the Swan).

Descending node   The point at which a satellite passes through the plane of the earth's equator on its journey southward.

Deviation   The amount of departure from normal values.

Directional antenna   Movable antenna which can be used to determine the direction from which radio signals are coming.

Dividers   Compasslike apparatus used to measure distances on a chart.

Eccentricity   The elongation of an ellipse; the distance of the principal focus from the center of the ellipse compared to the length of the semi-major axis.

Ellipse   The figure formed when a cone is cut by a plane not perpendicular to the axis of the cone.

Emulsion   The light-sensitive material coating the surface of a photographic film.

Equatorial bulge   The disproportionate increase in the earth's waistline over that of a perfect sphere.

Equatorial mounting   A mounting for a telescope in which the main (or polar) axis is parallel to the line joining the poles of the earth.

Equivalent focal length   The focal length of a lens system equal to that of a single lens.

Erfle eyepiece   A compound eyepiece of wide field.

Escape velocity   The velocity a body must attain to escape from the earth's gravitational field.

Exit pupil The diameter of the cone of light as it leaves the eyepiece of an optical instrument.

Exposure index The speed of a photographic emulsion, usually designated by an ASA number. Higher numbers mean faster, or more sensitive, film.

Eye relief Distance from the eye lens of an eyepiece to the point of sharpest focus.

Field of view Area covered by an optical instrument, expressed in feet per 1,000 yards or in degrees.

First surface mirror One in which the silvering material is placed on the exposed surface rather than in back, as in ordinary mirrors.

Focal length The distance from the surface of a lens or mirror to the point where parallel light rays intersect one another.

Focus The point at which the parallel rays are bent to a point.

Fovea centralis The point of sharpest vision of the eye, located on the retina at the back of the eyeball.

Frequency Number of waves passing a given point in an interval of one second.

Geodetic Measurements involving the surface of the earth.

Gravitational force The attractive force between two bodies located in space. The amount of this force depends on their masses and their distance apart.

Grid A system of intersecting lines used for plotting positions.

Heliograph Small mirror for reflecting the sun's rays for signaling purposes.

Hydrazine A compound of nitrogen which reacts with explosive violence when subjected to the action of concentrated nitric acid.

Image plane The area where rays from a lens or mirror come to a focus.

Inclination of the orbit The angle made by the plane of the elliptical path of a satellite with the plane of the earth's equator.

Inertia The resistance to change in velocity or direction shown by any object.

Instrument package The unit containing recording instruments, batteries, etc., placed in a satellite.

Intercept The point where the path of a satellite crosses any given line.

Ionosphere The layers of the atmosphere consisting of charged particles, located from 45 to 200 miles above the surface.

Latitude Distance on the globe measured in degrees north or south of the equator.

Lens system One or more lenses acting together and complementing each other for a common purpose. Example: the field and eye lens of an eyepiece.

Light trace   The line left on a photographic emulsion by the passage of a light source such as a star or satellite.

Longitude   Distance on the globe measured east or west of a great circle passing through Greenwich, England.

Lyman-Alpha line   A spectral line approximately in the middle of the ultra-violet spectrum.

Magnetic equator   A line around the earth at right angles to the magnetic north pole.

Magnetometers   Instruments used to measure the magnetic field of the earth.

Magnification   The amount by which an image appears closer to or larger than the object it represents.

Magnitude   The apparent brightness of stars or other heavenly bodies.

Major axis   The bisector of an ellipse that passes through both foci.

Mean motion   The average motion of a satellite moving in an elliptical path.

Megacycles   Millions of cycles per second, used as a measure of the frequencies of short waves.

Meridian   An imaginary line drawn through the heavens, from north to south, passing through the zenith.

Meteorite   Roughly, any meteoric particle weighing 10 milligrams (5/10,000 ounce) or more.

Micrometeorite   Any meteoric particle smaller than 10 milligrams.

Minitrack   A system of special radio stations set up to track satellites by means of their radio signals.

Minor axis   The bisector of an ellipse drawn at right angles to the line connecting their foci.

Moonbeam   The amateur organization set up to follow satellites by means of their radio signals.

Moonwatch   The amateur organization set up to track satellites visually.

Nautical twilight   The period, at dawn and dusk, when the sun is less than 12° below the horizon.

Nodal passage   The passage of a satellite through the imaginary plane formed by the extension of the earth's equatorial plane.

Objective lens   The main, or front, lens of a telescope or binoculars.

Optical axis   A line perpendicular to a lens and passing through its center.

Optical bench   Apparatus used to align the optical elements of a telescope.

Optical fence   An arrangement of telescopes covering an area of the sky in such a way that a passing satellite must be seen in at least one instrument.

Orbit   The track followed by one heavenly body as it revolves around another.

Oscilloscope A tube similar to a TV tube that measures wave variations.

Parabola The curved line formed when a plane, parallel to the side of a cone, intersects the cone.

Perigee The point in an orbit of a satellite when it comes closest to the main focus.

Perigee passage The time when a satellite passes overhead at its least distance from the surface of the earth.

Period of revolution Time for one complete revolution around the earth, usually measured from one nodal passage to another.

Perturbations Deviations of a satellite from its ideal orbit because of influences such as the earth's equatorial bulge, etc.

Photoelectric cell A cell that produces a current under the influence of sunshine.

Phototrack The amateur organization set up to track satellites photographically.

Planisphere The representation of the circles of a sphere on a plane, such as the adjustable star finders usually sold at planetariums.

Polar axis An axis parallel to the line connecting the north and south poles.

Power Synonym for "magnification."

Precession Real westward motion of the orbit of a satellite, as distinguished from the apparent westward motion caused by the earth's rotation to the east.

Principal focus The focus of an elliptical orbit that lies at the center of the body around which the satellite is moving.

Radiation Transfer of energy by wave motion, such as the emission of heat from a hot body like the sun.

Radius vector An imaginary line connecting a satellite at any point in its orbit with the principal focus.

Red shift The shift of the lines in a spectrograph toward the red end of the spectrum.

Right ascension The angular distance of any heavenly body eastward from a fixed point in the heavens called the vernal equinox. It is measured in time units rather than degrees.

Rod cells Special cells of the retina that are particularly sensitive to light.

Satellite Any smaller body revolving around a larger one.

Scan A telemetered transmission containing a complete sequence of channels.

Semimajor axis Half of a major axis of an ellipse.

Semiminor axis Half of a minor axis of an ellipse.

Solar flare A great protuberance arising from the sun's surface. It is most spectacular when seen at the edge of the sun.

Spectroscope   A prism device that separates the light from any object into its component colors.

Spherical aberration   The deficiency in a lens in which not all rays are bent to the same focus. It causes distortion of images at the edge of the field.

Sputnik   Russian word for satellite.

Statute mile   An earth mile (5,280 feet), as distinguished from a nautical mile (6,080 feet).

Sub-satellite point   The point on the earth's surface directly beneath the satellite at any point in its flight.

Synchronous clock   An electric clock calibrated to the cyclic pulses of the current used.

Tangent   The relationship of the two legs of a right triangle with respect to the size of the angle opposite one of them.

Telemetering   The process by which stored-up information may be relayed automatically to distant points.

Thermistor   A device sensitive to temperatures.

True anomaly   The angle subtended by a satellite in its passage from its perigee point to any other point in its orbit.

Twilight   See astronomical twilight; civil twilight; nautical twilight.

Universal time   The time at Greenwich, England. Clocks read an hour earlier for every 15 degrees west of this point and an hour later for every 15 degrees east of it. Since clocks on the eastern coast of the United States are approximately 75° west of Greenwich, they all read 5 hours earlier.

Vega   Principal star of the constellation Lyra.

Vernal equinox   The point where the sun crosses the celestial equator from south to north.

Wave length   The distance between any two successive crests in a series of waves.

Wide-angle   With reference to an apparent wide field of an eyepiece.

Wide-field   A wide area of view covered by binoculars or a telescope; roughly, any field greater than 10°.

Zenith   The point in the heavens directly above the observer.

Appendix II. Beginning of Morning Twilight

(To change the times given to standard time, add four minutes for each degree the observer is west of the standard meridian, or subtract four minutes for each degree the observer is east of the standard meridian. Standard meridians in the United States are 75°, 90°, 105°, and 120°. The data given here are for 1959. Subsequent tables may be obtained from the Superintendent of Documents, Washington 25, D.C.)

Date	0°	+10°	+20°	+30°	+35°	+40°	+45°	+50°	+52°	+54°	+56°	+58°	+60°
	h m	h m	h m	h m	h m	h m	h m	h m	h m	h m	h m	h m	h m
Jan. 0	4 44	5 01	5 15	5 30	5 36	5 44	5 51	6 00	6 02	6 06	6 10	6 14	6 18
10	4 49	5 05	5 19	5 32	5 39	5 46	5 53	5 59	6 02	6 05	6 09	6 12	6 16
20	4 54	5 08	5 21	5 32	5 38	5 44	5 49	5 55	5 57	5 59	6 02	6 05	6 07
30	4 58	5 10	5 21	5 30	5 35	5 39	5 42	5 47	5 48	5 49	5 51	5 52	5 53
Feb. 9	5 00	5 10	5 18	5 25	5 28	5 30	5 32	5 34	5 35	5 35	5 35	5 35	5 35
19	5 01	5 08	5 14	5 18	5 19	5 19	5 20	5 19	5 18	5 16	5 15	5 14	5 12
Mar. 1	5 00	5 05	5 08	5 08	5 08	5 06	5 03	4 59	4 58	4 55	4 52	4 49	4 45
11	4 58	5 00	5 00	4 58	4 55	4 51	4 45	4 38	4 34	4 30	4 25	4 20	4 13
21	4 55	4 55	4 52	4 45	4 40	4 34	4 26	4 15	4 09	4 03	3 56	3 48	3 38
31	4 52	4 49	4 42	4 32	4 25	4 17	4 05	3 50	3 42	3 34	3 24	3 12	2 58
Apr. 10	4 49	4 42	4 33	4 19	4 09	3 58	3 43	3 22	3 12	3 01	2 47	2 30	2 09
20	4 46	4 36	4 24	4 06	3 54	3 40	3 20	2 55	2 41	2 25	2 05	1 39	0 55
30	4 43	4 31	4 15	3 54	3 39	3 21	2 58	2 24	2 07	1 43	1 08	....	....
May 10	4 41	4 26	4 08	3 42	3 25	3 05	2 35	1 52	1 26	0 41	....	....	....
20	4 40	4 23	4 02	3 33	3 14	2 49	2 15	1 18	0 22	....	....	....	....
30	4 40	4 21	3 58	3 26	3 06	2 37	1 58	0 31	....	....	....	....	....
June 9	4 40	4 21	3 56	3 22	3 00	2 30	1 45	....	....	....	....	....	....
19	4 42	4 22	3 57	3 22	2 59	2 28	1 40	....	....	....	....	....	....
29	4 44	4 24	3 59	3 25	3 01	2 30	1 43	....	....	....	....	....	....
July 9	4 46	4 27	4 03	3 30	3 08	2 38	1 55	....	....	....	....	....	....
19	4 48	4 31	4 08	3 37	3 17	2 49	2 11	0 59	....	....	....	....	....
29	4 50	4 34	4 14	3 45	3 27	3 03	2 31	1 39	1 00	....	....	....	....
Aug. 8	4 50	4 36	4 18	3 54	3 38	3 17	2 50	2 11	1 48	1 14	....	....	....
18	4 50	4 39	4 23	4 02	3 49	3 32	3 09	2 38	2 22	2 02	1 34	0 47	....
28	4 48	4 40	4 28	4 11	3 59	3 45	3 27	3 03	2 50	2 36	2 18	1 55	1 23
Sept. 7	4 46	4 41	4 31	4 17	4 09	3 58	3 44	3 24	3 16	3 05	2 51	2 37	2 18
17	4 43	4 40	4 33	4 25	4 18	4 09	3 59	3 44	3 37	3 29	3 20	3 09	2 56
27	4 39	4 39	4 37	4 30	4 26	4 21	4 13	4 02	3 57	3 51	3 45	3 38	3 28
Oct. 7	4 36	4 38	4 39	4 37	4 34	4 30	4 26	4 19	4 16	4 12	4 07	4 02	3 56
17	4 32	4 39	4 41	4 42	4 42	4 41	4 38	4 35	4 33	4 30	4 28	4 25	4 21
27	4 31	4 38	4 45	4 49	4 50	4 50	4 51	4 50	4 50	4 48	4 48	4 46	4 45
Nov. 6	4 29	4 39	4 48	4 55	4 58	5 01	5 03	5 05	5 06	5 06	5 06	5 07	5 07
16	4 28	4 41	4 52	5 01	5 07	5 10	5 15	5 19	5 21	5 22	5 24	5 25	5 27
26	4 29	4 44	4 57	5 09	5 14	5 21	5 26	5 32	5 34	5 37	5 39	5 42	5 44
Dec. 6	4 33	4 48	5 03	5 16	5 22	5 29	5 36	5 43	5 46	5 49	5 53	5 57	6 00
16	4 36	4 53	5 08	5 23	5 29	5 37	5 44	5 52	5 55	5 59	6 03	6 07	6 11
26	4 41	4 59	5 13	5 27	5 35	5 42	5 50	5 57	6 01	6 04	6 09	6 13	6 17
36	4 46	5 03	5 18	5 31	5 38	5 45	5 52	6 00	6 03	6 07	6 10	6 14	6 18

Twilight lasts all night at latitude +60°, Apr. 23–Aug. 22; +58°, Apr. 29–Aug. 16; +56°, May 6–Aug. 9; +54°, May 13–Aug. 2; +52°, May 22–July 24; +50°, June 2–July 12.

Appendix III. Ending of Evening Twilight

(To change the times given to standard time, add four minutes for each degree the observer is west of the standard meridian, or subtract four minutes for every degree the observer is east of the standard meridian. Standard meridians in the United States are 75°, 90°, 105°, and 120°. The data given here are for 1959. Subsequent tables may be obtained from the Superintendent of Documents, Washington 25, D.C.)

Date		0°	+10°	+20°	+30°	+35°	+40°	+45°	+50°	+52°	+54°	+56°	+58°	+60°
		h m	h m	h m	h m	h m	h m	h m	h m	h m	h m	h m	h m	h m
Jan.	0	19 22	19 04	18 50	18 35	18 29	18 21	18 14	18 06	18 03	18 00	17 55	17 52	17 48
	10	19 25	19 10	18 56	18 43	18 36	18 29	18 23	18 16	18 13	18 10	18 07	18 03	18 00
	20	19 28	19 14	19 01	18 49	18 44	18 39	18 33	18 28	18 26	18 23	18 21	18 19	18 16
	30	19 29	19 17	19 06	18 57	18 53	18 49	18 45	18 42	18 41	18 40	18 38	18 37	18 35
Feb.	9	19 29	19 19	19 11	19 04	19 02	19 00	18 58	18 57	18 57	18 57	18 56	18 57	18 57
	19	19 27	19 20	19 15	19 11	19 11	19 11	19 11	19 12	19 13	19 15	19 16	19 18	19 20
Mar.	1	19 25	19 21	19 18	19 19	19 19	19 21	19 24	19 29	19 30	19 34	19 37	19 40	19 45
	11	19 22	19 21	19 21	19 24	19 28	19 32	19 38	19 45	19 49	19 54	19 59	20 05	20 12
	21	19 20	19 21	19 24	19 32	19 37	19 43	19 52	20 03	20 09	20 16	20 23	20 32	20 42
	31	19 17	19 21	19 28	19 39	19 46	19 56	20 08	20 23	20 31	20 40	20 50	21 02	21 17
Apr.	10	19 14	19 22	19 32	19 46	19 56	20 08	20 23	20 44	20 55	21 06	21 21	21 38	22 01
	20	19 12	19 23	19 36	19 54	20 06	20 22	20 41	21 08	21 22	21 38	22 00	22 28	23 19
	30	19 12	19 24	19 41	20 03	20 18	20 36	21 00	21 34	21 53	22 18	22 55	. . . .	. . . .
May	10	19 12	19 27	19 46	20 12	20 29	20 51	21 20	22 04	22 32	23 23			
	20	19 13	19 30	19 52	20 21	20 40	21 05	21 40	22 40	23 53				
	30	19 15	19 34	19 58	20 29	20 51	21 19	21 59	23 32					
June	9	19 18	19 37	20 02	20 36	20 59	21 29	22 15						
	19	19 20	19 40	20 05	20 40	21 03	21 35	22 23						
	29	19 22	19 42	20 07	20 41	21 05	21 36	22 23						
July	9	19 24	19 42	20 06	20 39	21 02	21 31	22 14						
	19	19 24	19 41	20 04	20 34	20 55	21 21	21 58	23 09					
	29	19 23	19 39	19 59	20 26	20 44	21 08	21 39	22 30	23 05				
Aug.	8	19 21	19 35	19 53	20 16	20 32	20 52	21 18	21 56	22 19	22 50			
	18	19 18	19 29	19 44	20 04	20 18	20 35	20 56	21 26	21 41	22 01	22 27	23 09	
	28	19 15	19 23	19 34	19 51	20 02	20 16	20 33	20 57	21 09	21 23	21 40	22 01	22 31
Sept.	7	19 11	19 16	19 25	19 37	19 47	19 57	20 11	20 29	20 38	20 48	21 01	21 15	21 33
	17	19 07	19 10	19 15	19 24	19 30	19 39	19 49	20 02	20 09	20 17	20 25	20 36	20 48
	27	19 03	19 03	19 05	19 11	19 15	19 20	19 28	19 38	19 43	19 48	19 54	20 01	20 10
Oct.	7	19 00	18 58	18 57	18 58	19 01	19 04	19 08	19 14	19 18	19 22	19 26	19 30	19 36
	17	18 59	18 52	18 50	18 48	18 48	18 49	18 51	18 53	18 55	18 58	19 00	19 03	19 07
	27	18 57	18 49	18 43	18 38	18 37	18 36	18 36	18 36	18 36	18 37	18 37	18 38	18 40
Nov.	6	18 58	18 48	18 39	18 31	18 28	18 25	18 23	18 20	18 20	18 19	18 18	18 18	18 17
	16	19 01	18 48	18 36	18 27	18 21	18 18	18 13	18 09	18 06	18 05	18 04	18 02	18 00
	26	19 05	18 49	18 36	18 25	18 19	18 12	18 07	18 01	17 58	17 56	17 53	17 50	17 47
Dec.	6	19 10	18 53	18 38	18 25	18 18	18 12	18 05	17 57	17 54	17 51	17 48	17 44	17 40
	16	19 14	18 57	18 42	18 27	18 21	18 14	18 06	17 57	17 55	17 51	17 47	17 43	17 39
	26	19 19	19 02	18 47	18 32	18 26	18 18	18 11	18 02	17 59	17 55	17 51	17 48	17 43
	36	19 24	19 07	18 52	18 39	18 32	18 25	18 18	18 10	18 08	18 04	18 00	17 56	17 53

Twilight lasts all night at latitude +60°, Apr. 23–Aug. 22; +58°, Apr. 29–Aug. 16; +56°, May 6–Aug. 9; +54°, May 13–Aug. 2; +52°, May 22–July 24; +50°, June 2–July 12.

Appendix IV. Time Signals

A. Time signals are normally broadcast from the following stations:

Station call letters	Frequencies of Transmission (in megacycles)
WWV	2.5, 5.0, 10.0, 15.0, 20.0, 25.0
WWVH	5.0, 10.0, 15.0, 20.0
GIC 37	17.685
GUAM	17.530
LOL	17.180
NSS	5.870, 9.4250, 12.8040, 17.050
NBA	17.127
NTG	17.055
GBZ	19.6
TQG5	13.873
CHU	7.335

B. Characteristics of CBU (Dominion Observatory, Canada) time signals:

00:00	Beginning of minutes (indicated by long tone)
00:01-00:28	Single tone for each second
00:29	This tone interval omitted
00:30-00:50	Single tone for each second
00:50-00:59	Voice announcement: "Dominion Observatory, Canada. Eastern Standard Time, _____ hours, _____ minutes"

C. Characteristics of WWV and WWVH (National Bureau of Standards stations) time signals:

(This sequence repeated every five minutes)

00:00	Tone begins
00:00	Double tick
00:01-00:58	Tone plus ticks each second
00:59	Tick omitted, but tone continues
01:00	Tone continues, plus double tick
01:00-01:58	Tone plus ticks each second
01:59	Tick omitted, but tone continues
02:00	Tone continues, plus double tick
02:01-02:58	Tone plus ticks each second
02:59	Tick omitted
03:00	Tone ends; double tick
03:01-03:58	Single tick each second
03:59	Tick omitted
04:00	Double tick
04:01-04:58	Single tick each second. During this interval, an announcement is made of Eastern Standard Time at 04:30. At 04:40 the Greenwich Mean Time is given in International Code. At 04:55 an announcement is made of Eastern Standard Time.
04:59	Tick omitted
05:00	Double tick, and tone recommences

Appendix V. Source of Materials

Moonwatch Telescopes:

Edscorp Satellite Telescope	(12° field, 51-mm objective, 5.5 power, 7-mm exit pupil, adjustable stand. Price, $49.50)
"Satelliter" Telescope	(12° field, 2-inch objective, 5 power, slight distortion at outer edges of field, has no mount. Price, $9.95)
Mounting for above	(Does not work as easily as standard Moonwatch mounts but is useful for satellite viewing by an individual observer. Price, $6.00. If equipped with mirror and bracket, $9.00)

(Edmund Scientific Company, Barrington, New Jersey)

Radio Shack Telescope	(10° field, 51-mm objective, 7 power, 7-mm exit pupil, adjustable stand. Price, $32.95)

(Radio Shack Corporation, 167 Washington Street, Boston 3, Massachusetts)

Gotoscope Super	(12° field, 6 power, erect image, equatorial mounting, setting circles. Price, $121.50)
Gotoscope Junior	(10° field, 5 power, altazimuth mount. Price, $39.00)

(Goto Optical Manufacturing Co., 1-115 Shimmachi, Setagaya-Ku, Tokyo, Japan)

Explorer	(11° field, 50-mm objective, 6.2 power, 8-mm exit pupil, altitude scale, mounted. Price, $49.50)

(Lafayette Radio, P.O. Box 651, Jamaica 31, New York)

Materials and Supplies for Moonwatch Telescopes:

Edmund Scientific Company, Barrington, New Jersey
A. Jaegers, 691 Merrick Road, Lynbrook, New York
Ashdowne Bros., 18450 Grand River, Detroit 23, Michigan
Nye Optical Company, 2100 Cherry Avenue, Long Beach 6, California
Garth Optical Company, P.O. Box 991, Springfield 1, Massachusetts
Precision Optical Supply Company, 1001 East 163 Street, New York 59, New York

Telescopes and Supplies:

REFLECTORS:

Cave Optical Company, 4137 Anaheim Street, Long Beach 4, California
Coast Instrument, Inc., 4811 Long Beach Boulevard, Long Beach 5, California
Stellar Scientific Instruments Co., 1015 West 6 Street, Santa Ana, California
O. Magnusson, 14570 West 52 Street, Arvada, Colorado
Criterion Manufacturing Company, 331 Church Street, Hartford 1, Connecticut
Sky-Scope Company, Inc., 475 Fifth Avenue, New York 17, New York

REFRACTORS:

Unitron Instrument, Division of United Scientific Company, 204-206 Milk Street, Boston 9, Massachusetts

CATADIOPTRIC TELESCOPES:

Questar Corporation, New Hope, Pennsylvania
J. W. Fecker, Inc., 6592 Hamilton Avenue, Pittsburgh 6, Pennsylvania

CHARTS, BOOKS, MAPS, ETC.:

Sky Publishing Company, Harvard College Observatory, Cambridge 38, Massachusetts
Astronomy Charted, 33 Winfield Street, Worcester 10, Massachusetts
Herbert A. Luft, 69-11 229 Street, Oakland Gardens 64, New York
General Astronautics Corporation, 11 West 42 Street, New York 36, New York
Library of Science, 59 Fourth Avenue, New York 3, New York

Appendix VI. Recommended Books
About Satellites and Space

Adler, Irving, *Man-Made Moons*. John Day Company, New York, 1957.

Bates, D. R., *Space Research and Exploration*. William Sloane Associates, Inc., New York, 1957.

Beeland, L., and Wells, R., *Space Satellite, Story of the Man-Made Moon*. Prentice-Hall, Inc., New York, 1957.

Bergaust, Eric, and Beller, William, *Satellite!* Doubleday and Company, Inc., Garden City, New York, 1956.

Branley, Franklyn M., *Exploring by Satellite*. Thomas Y. Crowell Company, New York, 1957.

Burgess, E., *Satellites and Spaceflight*. Macmillan Company, New York, 1958.

Caidin, Martin, *Vanguard, the Story of the First Man-Made Satellite*. E. P. Dutton & Company, New York, 1957.

Clarke, Arthur C., *Making of a Moon*. Harper & Brothers, New York, 1957.

Gatland, Kenneth W., ed., *Project Satellite*. British Book Centre, New York, 1958.

Leonard, Jonathan Norton, *Flight into Space*. Random House, Inc., New York, 1953.

Lewellen, John, *Earth Satellite*. Alfred A. Knopf, Inc., New York, 1957.

Ley, Willy, *Space Stations*. Simon and Schuster, Inc., New York, 1958.

Moore, Patrick, *Earth Satellites*. W. W. Norton & Company, Inc., New York, 1956.

Oberth, Hermann, *Man into Space*. Harper & Brothers, New York, 1956.

Ryan, Cornelius, ed., *Conquest of the Moon*. Viking Press, New York, 1953.

Van Allen, James, *Scientific Uses of Earth Satellites*. University of Michigan Press, Ann Arbor, Michigan, 1956.

Von Braun, Wernher, *Mars Project*. University of Illinois Press, Urbana, Illinois, 1953.

Appendix VII. Some Simple Formulas

A. Magnification of a telescope

$$M = \frac{f_o}{f_e}$$

M = magnification
f_o = focal length of objective lens
f_e = focal length of eyepiece

B. Exit pupil

$$EP = \frac{A f_e}{f_o}$$

EP = diameter of exit pupil
A = diameter of objective
f_e = focal length of eyepiece
f_o = focal length of objective

C. Eye relief

$$ER = bfl + f_e^2/f_o$$

bfl = back focal length of eyepiece (distance from the last surface of a lens or a system of lenses to the focus of parallel incoming rays)
f_e = focal length of eyepiece
f_o = focal length of objective

D. True field

$$TF = \frac{AF}{M}$$

TF = true field (in degrees)
AF = apparent field of eyepiece (in degrees)
M = magnification

Appendix VIII. The Greek Alphabet

A	α	Alpha	H	η	Eta	N	ν	Nu	T	τ	Tau
B	β	Beta	Θ	θ	Theta	Ξ	ξ	Xi	Υ	υ	Upsilon
Γ	γ	Gamma	I	ι	Iota	O	o	Omicron	Φ	ϕ	Phi
Δ	δ	Delta	K	κ	Kappa	Π	π	Pi	X	χ	Chi
E	ϵ	Epsilon	Λ	λ	Lambda	P	ρ	Rho	Ψ	ψ	Psi
Z	ζ	Zeta	M	μ	Mu	Σ	σ	Sigma	Ω	ω	Omega

Appendix IX. Table of Tangents

Degree	Tangent	Degree	Tangent	Degree	Tangent
0	.000	31	.601	61	1.80
1	.017	32	.625	62	1.88
2	.035	33	.649	63	1.96
3	.052	34	.675	64	2.05
4	.070	35	.700	65	2.14
5	.087	36	.727	66	2.25
6	.105	37	.754	67	2.36
7	.123	38	.781	68	2.48
8	.141	39	.810	69	2.61
9	.158	40	.839	70	2.75
10	.176	41	.869	71	2.90
11	.194	42	.900	72	3.08
12	.213	43	.933	73	3.27
13	.231	44	.966	74	3.49
14	.249	45	1.000	75	3.73
15	.268	46	1.03	76	4.01
16	.287	47	1.07	77	4.33
17	.306	48	1.11	78	4.70
18	.325	49	1.15	79	5.14
19	.344	50	1.19	80	5.67
20	.364	51	1.23	81	6.31
21	.384	52	1.28	82	7.12
22	.404	53	1.33	83	8.14
23	.424	54	1.38	84	9.51
24	.445	55	1.43	85	11.4
25	.466	56	1.48	86	14.3
26	.488	57	1.54	87	19.1
27	.510	58	1.60	88	28.6
28	.532	59	1.66	89	57.3
29	.554	60	1.73	90	∞
30	.577				

Appendix X. Phototrack Camera Elevation Above Horizon

For Given Angular Distance (DNA) and Satellite Height in Miles or Kilometers

Height Kilometers	Angular Distance to Sub-Satellite Point (DNA) in Degrees of Arc													Height Statute Miles
	0.0°	0.5°	1.0°	1.5°	2.0°	2.5°	3.0°	3.5°	4.0°	4.5°	5.0°	5.5°	6.0°	
64	90.0	48.7	29.4	20.2	15.0	11.7	09.4	07.6	06.2	05.0	04.1	03.2	02.5	40
97	90.0	63.2	44.6	33.0	25.6	20.6	17.0	14.2	12.1	10.3	08.8	07.6	06.5	70
161	90.0	70.4	54.5	42.8	34.5	28.5	23.9	20.4	18.5	15.3	13.4	11.8	10.4	100
209	90.0	74.6	61.1	50.2	41.8	35.2	30.1	26.1	22.8	20.1	17.8	15.8	14.1	130
257	90.0	77.3	65.7	55.8	47.6	41.0	35.6	31.2	27.5	24.5	21.9	19.6	17.7	160
306	90.0	79.2	69.1	60.0	52.3	45.8	40.3	35.7	31.8	28.5	25.7	23.2	21.1	190
354	90.0	80.6	71.6	63.4	56.1	49.8	44.4	39.7	35.7	32.3	29.2	26.6	24.3	220
402	90.0	81.6	73.6	66.1	59.3	53.2	47.9	43.3	39.2	35.6	32.5	29.7	27.3	250
451	90.0	82.5	75.2	68.3	61.9	56.2	51.0	46.4	42.3	38.7	35.5	32.6	30.1	280
498	90.0	83.1	76.4	70.1	64.1	58.6	53.7	49.2	45.1	41.5	38.3	35.3	32.7	310
547	90.0	83.7	77.5	71.6	66.0	60.8	56.0	51.6	47.7	44.1	40.8	37.8	35.1	340
595	90.0	84.2	78.4	72.9	67.6	62.7	58.1	53.8	49.9	46.4	43.1	40.1	37.4	370
644	90.0	84.6	79.2	74.0	69.0	64.3	59.9	55.8	52.0	48.5	45.2	42.3	39.5	400
692	90.0	84.9	79.9	75.0	70.3	65.8	61.6	57.5	53.8	50.4	47.2	44.2	41.5	430
740	90.0	85.2	80.5	75.8	71.3	67.1	63.0	59.1	55.5	52.1	49.0	46.0	43.3	460
789	90.0	85.5	81.0	76.6	72.3	68.2	64.3	60.6	57.0	53.7	50.6	47.7	45.0	490
837	90.0	85.7	81.4	77.2	73.2	69.2	65.5	61.9	58.4	55.2	52.2	49.3	46.6	520
885	90.0	85.9	81.8	77.8	73.9	70.2	66.5	63.0	59.7	56.6	53.6	50.7	48.1	550
	0.0°	0.5°	1.0°	1.5°	2.0°	2.5°	3.0°	3.5°	4.0°	4.5°	5.0°	5.5°	6.0°	
966	90.0	86.2	82.4	78.7	75.1	71.5	68.1	64.8	61.6	58.6	55.7	52.9	50.3	600
1127	90.0	86.7	83.4	80.1	76.9	73.7	70.6	67.6	64.7	61.9	59.2	56.6	54.1	700
1287	90.0	87.0	84.1	81.1	78.2	75.4	72.6	69.8	67.1	64.6	62.0	59.6	57.2	800
1448	90.0	87.3	84.6	81.9	79.3	76.7	74.1	71.6	69.1	66.7	64.3	62.0	59.8	900
1609	90.0	87.5	85.0	82.6	80.1	77.7	75.3	73.0	70.7	68.4	66.2	64.0	61.9	1000
1770	90.0	87.7	85.4	83.1	80.8	78.6	76.4	74.2	72.0	69.9	67.8	65.7	63.7	1100

Height Kilometers	7.0°	8.0°	9.0°	10.0°	11.0°	12.0°	13.0°	14.0°	15.0°	16.0°	17.0°	18.0°	Height Statute Miles
64	01.2	00.1	...										40
97	04.6	03.1	01.8	00.7									70
161	08.0	06.1	04.5	03.1	01.9	00.8							100
209	11.3	09.0	07.1	05.5	04.0	02.7	01.6	00.5					130
257	14.4	11.8	09.6	07.7	06.1	04.6	03.4	02.2	01.1	0			160
306	17.4	14.5	12.1	10.0	08.1	06.6	05.1	03.8	02.6	01.5	00.4		190
354	20.3	17.1	14.1	12.1	10.2	08.4	06.8	05.4	04.1	02.9	01.7	00.7	220
402	23.1	19.6	16.7	14.3	12.1	10.2	08.6	07.0	05.6	04.3	03.1	01.9	250
451	25.7	22.0	18.9	16.3	14.0	12.0	10.2	08.5	07.0	05.6	04.4	03.2	280
498	28.1	24.3	21.1	18.3	15.9	13.7	11.8	10.0	08.5	07.0	05.6	04.4	310
547	30.4	26.5	23.1	20.2	17.6	15.4	13.4	11.5	09.9	08.3	06.9	05.6	340
595	32.6	28.6	25.0	22.0	19.4	17.0	14.9	13.0	11.2	09.6	08.1	06.7	370
644	34.7	30.5	26.9	23.8	21.0	18.6	16.4	14.4	12.5	10.9	09.3	07.9	400
692	36.6	32.4	28.7	25.5	22.6	20.1	17.8	15.7	13.9	12.2	10.7	09.0	430
740	38.4	34.1	30.4	27.1	24.2	21.6	19.2	17.1	15.1	13.3	11.7	10.1	460
789	40.1	35.8	32.0	28.6	25.7	23.0	20.6	18.4	16.4	14.5	12.8	11.2	490
837	41.7	37.4	33.5	30.1	27.1	24.4	21.9	19.6	17.6	15.7	13.9	12.2	520
855	43.2	38.9	35.0	31.6	28.5	25.7	23.2	20.9	18.7	16.8	15.0	13.3	550
	7.0°	8.0°	9.0°	10.0°	11.0°	12.0°	13.0°	14.0°	15.0°	16.0°	17.0°	18.0°	
966	45.5	41.2	37.3	33.8	30.7	27.8	25.2	22.8	20.6	18.6	16.7	15.0	600
1127	49.5	45.3	41.4	37.8	34.6	31.7	29.0	26.5	24.2	22.0	20.0	18.1	700
1287	52.8	48.7	44.9	41.3	38.1	35.1	32.3	29.7	27.4	25.1	23.0	21.1	800
1448	55.5	51.6	47.8	44.4	41.1	38.1	35.3	32.7	30.3	28.0	25.8	23.8	900
1609	57.9	54.0	50.4	47.0	43.8	40.8	38.0	35.4	32.9	30.6	28.4	26.3	1000
1770	59.9	56.2	52.6	49.3	46.2	43.2	40.4	37.8	35.3	32.9	30.7	28.6	1100

Index